Good

Other titles by

ANNE MATHER
IN HARLEQUIN PRESENTS

Other titles by

ANNE MATHER
IN HARLEQUIN ROMANCES

Many of these titles, and other titles in the
Harlequin Romance series, are available at your
local bookseller or through the Harlequin Reader
Service. For a free catalogue listing all available
Harlequin Presents and Harlequin Romances,
send your name and address to:

HARLEQUIN READER SERVICE,
M.P.O. Box 707
Niagara Falls, N.Y. 14302

Canadian address:
Stratford, Ontario, Canada N5A 6W2
or use coupon at back of book.

ANNE MATHER

rachel trevellyan

Harlequin Books

TORONTO • LONDON • NEW YORK • AMSTERDAM
SYDNEY • HAMBURG • PARIS

Harlequin Presents edition published March 1975
ISBN 0-373-70586-7

Second printing October 1977
Third printing March 1979

Original hardcover edition published in 1974
by Mills & Boon Limited

Printed in Canada

CHAPTER ONE

HE was tired, very tired. The road through Cornwall had not been at all what he had expected after the long, fast-moving roads of his own country, and it had slowed his progress considerably. It was now after eight o'clock, darkness had fallen, and to add to his difficulties a sea fret was making the road ahead very hard to distinguish even with powerful headlights.

From Launceston the road had twisted and turned narrowly, an annoyance to the most patient of drivers, which he would be the first to admit he was not, and since leaving Penzance it had deteriorated into little more than a country lane. A series of sharp bends and precipitous summits had kept him continually in a low gear, and demanded all his concentration.

Occasionally, it had occurred to him that he was a fool, that he should not have agreed to undertake this journey at this time of the year. Although it was spring back home, it was still winter here even in this southern corner of England. But his mother had been so persuasive that he had not had the heart to refuse her. Apparently, Malcolm Trevellyan's family had been kind to her in the past, and now that Malcolm was ill it was only natural that she should want to try and repay that kindness in some way. It was a long time since he had seen his mother so agitated about anything, and he had submitted to her demands for urgency.

He realised, too, that in spite of his mother's almost total adaptation to the Portuguese way of life, since his father's death two years ago she sometimes felt lonely and perhaps longed for someone from her native country to talk to.

He consulted the broad gold watch on its plain leather strap which encircled his wrist under the cuff of his plain grey suede jacket. Surely it could not be much further to Mawvry. His mother had said it was about ten miles from Penzance, which in the measurements he was used to meant something over sixteen kilometres. But on these roads and in these conditions it had seemed much further.

He began considering the arrangements he had made to transfer Malcolm Trevellyan to Mendao. Trevellyan was not a young man, and disabled into the bargain. He had had a severe attack of thrombosis two months ago which had left him partially paralysed and therefore unable to walk. But he was capable of riding in the back of a car, and that was why he had had this luxurious limousine made available to him at London Airport. Tomorrow they would make the return journey to London, board the plane for Lisbon, and be in Mendao by late afternoon. It was as simple as that. He did not want to stay longer. He had his own reasons for wishing to return to his estate as soon as possible. And once at the Quinta Martinez, Malcolm Trevellyan would want for nothing—his mother would see to that.

A signpost loomed out of the mist and the word *Mawvry* could clearly be seen. He sighed with relief. He was here at last. Now all he had to do was find the house of Malcolm Trevellyan.

The village was small, and when he parked the car in the square and slid stiffly from behind the driving wheel, the tang of salt filled his nostrils. Obviously he must be very near the sea, but at the moment the mist shrouded everything but his immediate surroundings.

Across the square a swinging sign indicated a tavern which appeared to be doing good business judging from the noise from within, and deciding it would be simpler to enquire the whereabouts of Malcolm Trevellyan's house rather than attempting to find it he pulled a fur-lined jacket from the back of his car. Sliding his arms into the sleeves, he crossed the square, his collar turned up against the weather. He shivered. Even in the coldest months Mendao was not like this, and he thought with longing of the baroque beauty of the *quinta*, the lush valley in which it was situated, and the vivid blueness of the ocean that lapped not too many miles away. It would have been so much easier, he thought, not to have come himself; to have sent Alonzo Diaz or Juan d'Almera. But his mother had been curiously determined that he should be the one, and he imagined she wanted Malcolm Trevellyan to know that her invitation was a personal one.

The noise in the thick, smoky atmosphere of the bar decreased almost immediately when he pushed open the door. He felt the wave of curiosity that swept over the room, a sense of almost alien hostility.

He made his way to the bar and stood there, tall and dark, taller and darker than most of these dark Cornishmen. Speaking in slightly accented English, he said: 'Pardon me, but could you direct me to the house of a Senhor Malcolm Trevellyan?'

The bartender stopped polishing the glass in his hand and he could have sworn the hostility around him strengthened.

'And who might be asking?' queried the bartender.

He sighed. 'My name is unimportant. It would mean nothing to you. But I do wish to see Senhor Trevellyan, and as it is such an unpleasant evening, I thought perhaps——'

'Folks round here don't care to pass information to —foreigners,' remarked a leathery-faced man on his right.

He controlled his annoyance with difficulty. 'I assure you, my business with Senhor Trevellyan is perfectly respectable. He is expecting me. But the mist obliterates almost everything——'

The bartender glanced round at the avid faces about them and seemed to come to a decision. 'You come in on the Penzance road?'

'I suppose I did.'

'Then you passed the Trevellyan place. 'Bout a mile back. Set off the road, it is, overlooking the sea.'

'I'm very grateful. Thank you.'

He bowed his head politely and turned to go, but his way was barred by a husky young fisherman.

'What business you got with old Trevellyan?' he demanded belligerently. 'Are you sure it's not Rachel you come to see?'

'Rachel?' He frowned. 'I'm afraid I know no one of that name.'

'And you say you know Malcolm Trevellyan?' The young man's lip curled. 'How can you know him and not Rachel?'

He thrust his hands deep into the pockets of his coat. 'Who is Rachel, might I ask?' He felt a stirring of unease.

The young man glanced round at his comrades. 'Shall I tell him?'

An older man tugged at his sleeve. 'Let him go, Bart. Maybe this is some business deal. Maybe he doesn't know Rachel.'

His jaw felt taut. 'Please,' he said. 'Enlighten me. Who is Rachel?'

'Rachel's his wife, of course,' snapped the young fisherman grimly. 'Didn't you know?'

'I'm afraid I did not.'

'Bart!' The older man dragged the younger one aside. 'Leave it, boy. It's no business of ours.'

8

'Isn't it? Isn't it? Don't you care what happens to Rachel?'

'Of course I care——' The older man was answering, but he waited to hear no more. Pressing his way through the throng of hostile faces, he reached the door and thrusting it open stepped out into the freezing air. In this instance the cold was a relief, infinitely preferable to the heat of the bar.

But as he walked back to the car his brain buzzed with the information he had just been presented. Malcolm Trevellyan was married! He had never mentioned it. In all Trevellyan's correspondence with his mother, there had been no reference made to a wife. On the contrary, he recalled his mother's comments that Malcolm had become a confirmed bachelor, and certainly four years ago when she and his father had visited England he had had no wife then.

The sense of unease increased. What did it mean? Had Trevellyan married some widow for companionship in his latter years? And if so, why hadn't he told them? Or did he expect they knew? Did he presume the invitation he had received included his wife, too?

He shook his head and opening the car door slid back behind the wheel. How would his mother react if that were so? Would she want another woman at the *quinta*? The invitation extended to Trevellyan had been an open one, but if he had a wife...

And what was the young fisherman's interest in all this? Why were they so hostile to the name Trevellyan? Was it possible that the man Bart might be this unknown Rachel's son?

He felt angry suddenly. He was cold and tired, a stranger in a strange country, and right now he wished he had booked in at a hotel in Penzance and left the return journey until two days hence.

Leaving the village square, he turned back on to the

9

Penzance road. The mist had cleared slightly and he drove slowly, looking for the signs of a gatepost, some indication that a house lay back from the road.

He found it almost easily. There were no other houses in the area, and he turned between stone gateposts and ran up a narrow drive to where lights glinted from behind curtained windows He stopped the car and slid out, looking up at the stone façade of the building. It was not a large house, but in the gloom there was something faintly menacing about it. Shrugging off such fanciful feelings, he walked up the steps to the door and knocked.

There was silence for so long that he knocked again, but then there was the sound of bolts being drawn and he waited irritably for the door to be opened. *Deus*, he thought with impatience. Surely he had been expected even at this hour? In his mother's letter she had clearly stated the date and expected time of his arrival. Just because he was a little later than expected it should not mean that they had given him up, that they had bolted the door against him. *They?*

The door swung inward suddenly and in the light that was shed from the hall behind her he saw a girl. His first impression was of a glory of red-gold hair that tumbled in abundant confusion about an oval face. She was of medium height, but very slender which made her seem smaller. She was dressed in an old pair of denim trousers that clung to her like a second skin, and which, needless to say, would have horrified his mother and her friends, while the paint-daubed smock she wore with them revealed the slight swell of her breasts and the thinness of her arms. Who was this? He thought she looked about eighteen, but he could not be absolutely certain in this light. Long silky lashes brushed her cheeks and swept upward in surprise when she encountered his dark gaze. Had Malcolm Trevellyan a daughter as well as a wife?

'Yes?' She was abrupt.

He gave a slight bow and then wished he had not. But the Portuguese blood in his veins ran so much stronger than his English ancestry, and it was second nature to him to behave courteously.

'I wish to see Senhor Malcolm Trevellyan, *senhorita*,' he stated politely. 'I am Luis Martinez, Marquês de Mendao!'

The girl stared at him uncomprehendingly for a moment. It was obvious she hadn't the faintest idea who he was or that he was expected, and he felt reassured. Clearly she could not be a member of this household or she would have known. He had been beginning to think that Malcom Trevellyan had concealed a great deal from his mother.

'Won't you come in?'

The girl stood aside with obvious reluctance and Luis entered the narrow hall. There was a carpet on the floor, but it was threadbare in places, and while everything was clean there was little in the way of comfort. Certainly Malcolm Trevellyan deserved more salubrious surroundings than these to recuperate in.

The door was closed behind them and the girl indicated that he should enter a room on his right.

'If you'll wait a moment, I'll tell Malcolm you're here,' she said, rather stiffly.

Luis inclined his head. 'Thank you.' He allowed himself to be shown into a room which appeared to be a parlour. The door closed behind him and he looked about with interest.

In the poor light shed from a standard lamp which the girl had switched on at his entrance he saw that this room was rarely used. It had an unlived-in air, a mustiness about it, and the stiff-backed chairs and horsehair sofa were reminiscent of the kind of places

11

described in English literature of the nineteenth century. He had read a great deal of English literature when he was at the university.

Bric-à-brac lined the mantelshelf, and as a collector of antiques he ran a practised eye over them. But there was nothing there to interest the expert and he folded his hands behind his back and paced rather restlessly about the room.

A clock chimed somewhere in the house and he glanced again at his watch. It was half past nine. He had been travelling since very early that morning. No wonder he was beginning to feel weary and lacking in patience.

The door behind him opened suddenly and he swung round to confront the girl who stood in the aperture. There was a certain wary speculation in her eyes now and he wondered why. He wondered, too, what she was doing here at this time of night, and recalled belatedly that the doors had been bolted on his arrival. Why should she be staying here when she apparently knew so little of her host's affairs?

Seen in this light she was perhaps a little older than he had at first imagined. Twenty-one, maybe, or twenty-two; surely no more. In her casual clothes she was, he thought, a typical example of emancipated youth, and he pondered what his mother's reactions to her might be. Portuguese girls were not allowed to wear such attire; they were not allowed such freedom. They dressed conservatively. They retained, or so Luis had been brought up to believe, a certain detachment, an aura of mystery, that was only lifted to admit their betrothed, their chosen husband. He supposed there was a kind of Moorish influence still evident in his country that favoured the customs of the *seraglio*, the segregation of women both before and after marriage.

'If you'll come this way,' the girl said now, and Luis

unbuttoned his overcoat and nodded.

The girl led the way along the hall to a room at the back of the house which Luis suspected in daylight probably gave a view of the coastline. But tonight the curtains were drawn across the windows and the only light came from a lamp beside the huge double bed which dominated the room. There was an enormous fire burning in the wide grate which gave out an uncomfortable amount of heat, and propped on pillows in the middle of the tumbled bed was a figure in thick pyjamas who stared at him with piercing blue eyes.

Malcolm Trevellyan must have been about fifty, but he looked older. Thinning hair topped a face that was prematurely lined, and although he must once have been quite a big man now the fleshless skin hung on him.

Luis glanced round at the girl, who had remained by the door when he entered the room, and seeing that she was making no move to leave, he said: 'How do you do, Senhor Trevellyan. I am Luis Martinez, at your service. You were expecting me?'

'Of course. Of course. Come in.' Malcolm Trevellyan spoke welcomingly, his voice strong and imperative. 'Have you had a good journey? You're later than I expected, but I suppose the weather hasn't helped. Cold, isn't it? Not what you're used to, I suppose.'

'No.' Luis managed a faint smile. 'How are you, *senhor*?'

'Oh, I'll be all right. Got to take it easy, that's all.' He indicated his legs outlined beneath the bedcovers. 'Can't do much else at the moment.'

'I'm sorry.' Luis glanced back at the girl again. 'However, I am sure you will find Mendao a much less demanding climate.'

He heard the girl behind him catch her breath on a gasp, and suddenly the man seemed to remember she

13

was there. Waving his arms about with obvious annoyance, he snapped: 'Don't just stand there, Rachel! Go and make our guest some tea and sandwiches. I'm sure he could do with something after his journey!'

Luis felt a creeping sense of disbelief invading his senses. Trevellyan had called the girl Rachel. *Rachel!* And down at the tavern in the village, the young fisherman had angrily thrown the name of Trevellyan's wife at him and that had been Rachel, too. *Deus*, this girl could not be Trevellyan's wife, could she? He felt almost sickened at the thought.

He looked round, but she had gone, and suddenly he wished he had let Juan or Alonzo come here in his place. He wanted no part of this.

But he was here, he was committed, and he had to ask the inevitable question:

'That young woman, *senhor*? She is some relation of yours?'

Malcolm Trevellyan sniffed and gathered the rugs closer about him. 'I suppose you would say that. I have to talk to you about her, *senhor*.'

Luis folded his hands behind his back again. It was a favourite position of his and right now he had no desire to sit in this man's presence.

Malcolm Trevellyan seemed to realise that Luis was waiting for an explanation, and with a sigh, he began: 'Rachel is my wife, *senhor*.'

Luis felt the muscles of his face hardening. 'Indeed?'

'Yes, but please, let me explain.'

'You did not explain the situation to my mother, *senhor*.'

'I know, I know. And I'm sorry. But there was no way I could, you see. It's something I needed to talk to you about, to discuss with you, to explain the circumstances——'

'What circumstances, *senhor*?'

14

Trevellyan tugged at the lobe of his ear. 'Rachel and I have been married three years, *senhor*. She was only eighteen at that time, and her father had just died.' He shook his head. 'I am not one to judge people, but Rachel was a trial to her father. Poor man, he did not know how to deal with her. She's an artist, *senhor*, and perhaps even in your country you know what artists are. They like to call themselves free-living individuals. For free-living, substitute free-loving, and there you have their way of life in a nutshell.'

Luis's ring with its large inset emerald dug into his fingers. 'What are you trying to say, *senhor*?'

Trevellyan sighed. 'It's not easy, *senhor*. Rachel is my wife, and I love her. But I don't always understand her.'

'Go on!' Luis was impatient.

'Very well. At the time her father died, Rachel was pregnant. The man, whoever he was, had deserted her, and she was alone. Her father and I had always been friends and I couldn't see her destitute. I offered marriage on the understanding that she could continue with her painting, and she accepted. Unfortunately she miscarried, and the child was never born.'

'I see.' Luis felt a sense of distaste. 'And you could not tell my mother of this?'

'How could I? Is it something you could baldly write in a letter?'

'Perhaps not.' Luis shrugged his broad shoulders. 'So what do you expect her to do now?'

Trevellyan lay back weakly on his pillows. 'Rachel knows me, *senhor*. She knows my likes and dislikes, and she has cared for me, after her fashion. I wouldn't like to leave her here alone, at the mercy of her own weaknesses.'

'You are suggesting that—that your wife accompanies us to Mendao?'

The other man's eyes sought his appealingly. 'Would it be such a trial to you—to your mother? I promise you, she would cause no trouble.'

Luis could have almost laughed at the farcical aspects of this situation had it not been so serious. How could Trevellyan expect to control his wife from his bed—or even a wheelchair for that matter? Unless years of marriage with him had tempered her rebellious nature, destroyed the streak of wildness which had previously caused such unhappiness. He took a deep breath. Even after everything he had heard, the idea of that girl being married to Malcolm Trevellyan could make him feel physically sick. And he couldn't imagine why. It was nothing to do with him.

Now Luis ran a hand round the back of his neck, over the smooth black hair that brushed his collar. 'But it seemed obvious when I arrived that—that Senhora Trevellyan knew nothing of my reasons for being here.'

Trevellyan plucked at the bedcovers. 'I know, I know. I haven't mentioned my plans to her yet.'

'Why not?'

'How could I? I didn't even know whether you—or your mother—would permit her to accompany me.'

'I see.' Luis's hand fell to his side.

There were footsteps outside in the hall and presently the girl entered the room again carrying a tray. Luis's immediate instinct was to take the tray from her, but then he stood politely aside and allowed her to place it on the table beside the bed.

Malcolm Trevellyan seemed to come to a decision. 'Allow me to introduce you, *senhor*,' he said. 'This is my wife Rachel. Rachel, this is the son of a good friend of mine, Senhor Martinez.'

Rachel looked up at the tall dark Portuguese. 'Senhor Martinez introduced himself at the door,' she said, without expression in her voice.

Her husband sniffed. 'Is that all you have to say?' he demanded in a low tone, and Luis intercepted the look that passed between them and there was no friendliness in it. He felt repulsed. Repulsed by them, by this whole situation.

However, the girl seemed stung by her husband's contemptuous tone. Her voice when she spoke was low and attractive with little of the Cornish drawl evident in that of Malcolm Trevellyan. 'Why is he here, Malcolm?' she asked, rather heatedly. 'What did he mean earlier about you finding some foreign place less demanding than here? What's going on?'

Trevellyan looked to Luis for guidance and with a sigh Luis said: 'You may or may not be aware, *senhora*, that your husband's family cared for my mother many years ago when she was orphaned. Afterwards, she married a Portuguese, my father, but she and Senhor Trevellyan's family maintained a correspondence and in latter years she visited England with my father and met your husband again.'

The girl looked puzzled. 'I didn't know that, but what of it?'

Luis's lips thinned. He was not accustomed to being spoken to in that cursory manner, particularly not by such a slip of a girl.

'Naturally when—when your husband became ill, my mother was concerned about him. I must confess she did not know he had taken a wife, but nevertheless she suggested to Senhor Trevellyan that he might come to Portugal, to our estates at Mendao, to recuperate for a few weeks.'

'I see.' The girl's eyes were wide as she turned back to the man in the bed. 'Why didn't you tell me?'

Malcolm Trevellyan sniffed. 'I wasn't sure about the arrangements. I didn't want to—raise your hopes unnecessarily.'

'Raise my hopes?' She stared at him uncomprehendingly. 'You mean I can stay here?'

'No, that's not what I mean!' Trevellyan looked momentarily incensed. Then he calmed himself. 'I simply meant that I didn't want to raise your hopes about this holiday in Portugal until I was sure you would be welcome there.'

'A holiday in Portugal!' echoed the girl. 'I—I don't want to go to Portugal.'

Luis clenched his fists. 'Surely you would not allow your husband, a sick man, to travel there without your ministrations, *senhora*?'

The girl Rachel turned stormy green eyes in his direction. 'I'm sorry, *senhor*, if I sound ungrateful. But I can assure you my husband doesn't require my ministrations.'

'*Rachel!*' Trevellyan's face was grim. 'Stop this at once! If Senhor Martinez will overlook this unpleasantness, naturally you will accompany me to Portugal.'

Rachel Trevellyan's breast rose and fell with the tumult of her emotions. Animated like this, she was quite startlingly attractive and unwillingly Luis felt a sense of compassion for her. Whatever she had done in the past she had forfeited a great deal in becoming the wife of a man as old as Malcolm Trevellyan.

Then he inwardly chided himself. She had not been forced to marry him. A girl with more strength of mind, with more courage in her convictions, would have managed somehow, would have found a way to support herself and the unborn child. No, Rachel Trevellyan had taken the easy way out of a difficult situation and now resented the very person who had helped her most. Luis allowed contempt to replace his earlier compassion. Rachel Trevellyan deserved nothing else.

Malcolm Trevellyan shuffled across the bed. 'Come along, Rachel,' he said. 'Pour Senhor Martinez some tea, and stop behaving like a spoilt child.'

For a moment Luis thought she was about to refuse, but then, obediently it seemed, she lifted the teapot and poured the hot liquid into two cups. Turning to him, she said: 'Milk and sugar?'

'Thank you, sugar only,' he replied quietly, and she added two lumps before passing the cup to him.

'Do sit down, *senhor*.' Malcolm Trevellyan indicated a chair now, and although it was not his nature to sit in the presence of an adult female who happened to be standing Luis subsided into the cane chair by the bed.

Rachel poured her husband's tea, added milk and sugar, stirred it and then handed it to him. There were sandwiches on the tray too, and she proffered these, but Luis declined. He had had a late lunch on the way down, and although in his own country he could have enjoyed a late dinner, the idea of sandwiches did not appeal to him. In truth he wished he had made some arrangements to stay at a hotel, even though in the correspondence Malcolm Trevellyan had had with his mother he had suggested that Luis might stay here overnight; and now, late as it was with the mist outside and the evident lack of accommodation facilities nearby, he had no choice.

Rachel seemed to be on the point of leaving them, when her husband said: 'Well, *senhor*? What arrangements have you made? And what conclusion have you reached regarding—Rachel?'

That was difficult. What conclusion had he reached? Luis replaced his half empty cup on the tray. It was a decision he had never expected to have to make and he realised that had either Juan or Alonzo come here in his place they would have had to have deferred a decision until either his mother or himself had been informed.

As he was here things were different. If he were to contact his mother and discuss it with her, it would only worry her unnecessarily. After all, she could hardly withdraw her invitation at this late date, even taking the changed circumstances into account, and although he was well aware what her reactions to a young woman like Rachel Trevellyan would be, there was little he could do without disappointing Malcolm Trevellyan.

And there was not just his mother to consider at Mendao...

Rachel Trevellyan stood by the door. 'It's obvious that Senhor Martinez does not wish me to accompany you to Portugal, Malcolm, whatever he says,' she declared. 'Why can't I stay here? What harm would it do?'

Luis rose to his feet. Her attitude of dissension was reacting on him as an eagerness to accompany them would never have done. In his country women did not argue with their menfolk. They were mild and agreeable, totally feminine in every way. Rachel Trevellyan spoke without respect, assumed a responsibility for her own affairs which was not seemly in a young woman, let alone a wife.

'I have thought the matter over, *senhor*,' he said, addressing himself to Malcolm Trevellyan, 'and naturally my mother would wish me to extend our invitation to include your wife.'

There was a gulp from Rachel Trevellyan at this point, but Luis ignored her, keeping his eyes on the man in the bed. A look of gratification was spreading over Malcolm Trevellyan's features and he nodded in a satisfied way.

'Thank you, *senhor*, that's very civil of you. Very

civil indeed. And when Rachel gets used to the idea, she'll thank you, too, won't you, Rachel?'

Again a strange look passed between them, and Luis saw the girl visibly shrink. 'When do you expect me to be ready to leave?' she exclaimed helplessly. 'I've made no arrangements. What about a passport?'

Trevellyan fixed her with a stare. 'You forget, Rachel. You went abroad with your father only a year before he died. I happen to know your passport is still valid.'

'But—but I need time——'

'Why?'

'There are arrangements to be made——'

'What arrangements?'

She shook her head. 'Lots of things.'

'Rachel, all you need to do is pack a suitcase. We leave in the morning.'

'No!'

'Yes. Naturally, Senhor Martinez will stay here to-night——'

Now Luis felt uncomfortable. 'That's quite unnecessary,' he began automatically. 'I can stay at a hotel.'

'Nonsense,' exclaimed Trevellyan. 'Of course you'll stay here. It's the least we can do, isn't it, Rachel?'

'If you say so.' There was a lacklustre quality about her now.

Luis controlled a sigh. He wished it were morning already. He had no desire to spend a night here, conscious as he was of Rachel Trevellyan's resentment. But he could hardly refuse without throwing Malcolm Trevellyan's hospitality back in his face.

'I'll go and see about making up a bed,' said Rachel now, and her husband nodded.

'That's right. You can let us know when it's ready. I'm sure Senhor Martinez is tired after his journey.'

While Rachel was away, Malcolm asked about Luis's

21

mother, the Marquesa de Mendao. For a few moments at least, Luis relaxed. It was reassuring to speak about his mother. At least there were no undercurrents there. He removed his overcoat and sat comfortably in his chair, lighting a cheroot which he favoured when Malcolm produced cigarettes.

By the time Rachel returned Luis was feeling infinitely less tense, although the atmosphere changed again as soon as she entered the room.

'The room's ready,' she announced, and Luis stood up.

'I'll bid you goodnight, then,' said Malcolm, apparently indifferent to his wife's attitude. 'What time do you want us to leave in the morning?'

'I suggest we say as early as possible and leave it at that,' remarked Luis. 'Goodnight.'

'Goodnight.' Malcolm smiled, rather smugly, Luis thought, but then he accompanied Rachel from the room without another word.

They went upstairs and into a room at the front of the house. The rest of the building struck chill after the unpleasant heat of Malcolm Trevellyan's bedroom, but Luis saw that Rachel had turned on an electric fire in the room he was to occupy.

It was a large bedroom, sparsely furnished, with only a bed, a wardrobe, and a kind of washstand. The only floor covering was a rag rug beside the bed, but as with the rest of the house everything was spotlessly clean.

'I've put a hot water bottle in the bed,' said Rachel, remaining by the door when he advanced into the room. 'Is there anything else you need?'

Luis thought of his suitcase locked in the boot of his car, but shook his head. His eyes encountered hers. He had never seen such green eyes before and fringed as they were by long black lashes they seemed to overshadow her other features. The feeling of unease he had felt earlier stirred again and he didn't know why. Something told him he ought to call this off here and now and refuse to take either Malcolm Trevellyan or his wife back to his home in Mendao. But that was ridiculous, he told himself angrily. He was allowing weariness to make him fanciful. What possible harm could come from offering the Trevellyans their hospitality for a couple of weeks? His mother might not welcome Rachel's presence, she might take exception to her mode of dress, but surely that could be modified. For all her English upbringing, his mother's forty years in Portugal had made her typically Portuguese in outlook.

And if Amalia considered it unseemly to have a young woman, albeit a married one, staying in his house in these weeks before their wedding, then perhaps some other arrangements could be made within the confines of the estate.

He realised suddenly that he had been staring at Rachel for an unconscionably long period and that her cheeks had suffused with colour under his gaze.

Forcing his attention to other things, he said: 'Thank you, *senhora*. I have everything I need. I'm sure I shall be very comfortable.'

His voice was cool, but he couldn't help it. There was something about this girl that disturbed him, and it was a new experience for him. Normally he was in complete control of his reactions.

'Very well.' She made to close the door. 'Goodnight.'

'Goodnight, *senhora*.'

He gave a stiff little movement of his head and the door closed. But after she had gone, he was conscious that he would be unable to banish her so easily from his mind as from his sight.

CHAPTER TWO

SINCE leaving the coast, the road had wound through a series of lushly cultivated valleys, bright with blossoming trees and shrubs, scented with pine and citrus. Rachel saw vine-clad terraces, orchards of fig and almond trees, pergolas draped with the lemon-vine while the varied colours of bougainvillea rioted in every available space. She had never seen jacarandas growing wild before, or longed to touch the satin-soft petals of the oleander. It was all new and stimulating, and she could not entirely deny the rising sense of excitement that was stirring inside her. Her fingers itched to take her paintbrush and try, probably without success, she thought, to transfer some of this beauty and colour on to canvas. This was Portugal, the country of the lean, dark man seated beside her at the wheel of his luxurious silver limousine, the natural background of this aristocratic nobleman, this unexpected friend of Malcolm's, who regarded her with obvious contempt.

Her lips twisted and she shivered in spite of the heat of the day which had already forced her to shed the jacket of the slim-fitting cream slack suit she had worn to travel in. Her husband, overcome by the temperature, was asleep in the back of the limousine, but Luis Martinez, Marquês de Mendao, seemed totally unaffected by the climate.

She glanced surreptitiously towards him. His concentration was all on the road ahead and for a moment she was able to look at him unobserved. Who would have thought that in less than twenty-four hours her life could change so completely? Yesterday afternoon she had spent at her easel, trying to finish the portrait of one of the village children while Malcolm slept, aware of a certain excitement about him which she had not been able to explain. That the explanation had come in such a startling way was scarcely believable. And yet, last night, when she had opened the door and found the tall dark alien on the step, she had known that he was in some way responsible for that latent excitement. But even then she had not suspected that Malcolm intended to take her away.

She drew a trembling breath. He had wanted to do so, goodness knows, only circumstances had prevented it. Since his illness he had been almost fanatical in his attempts to keep her away from people she knew, but she had believed his hands had been tied. How he must have laughed to himself to think that the very thing which she had thought would keep them in Mawvry among her friends, among the people she knew and cared about, was the very thing which had provided the means to get them away.

The car braked smoothly at a bend where a narrow bridge negotiated a rippling stream below them. The water ran swiftly over smooth stones worn by the passage of time, and an enormous elm spread its branches casting avenues of shade. The lush green turf invited relaxation beside the stream where the sunlight dappled quiet pools and muted the birds' song. Rachel could have climbed out of the car then and paddled in that stream, and she sighed, attracting the attention of the man at her side.

'You are tired?' he queried politely, his clipped tones betraying a certain impatience.

Rachel shook her head. 'No. Not tired.' She did not add *senhor*, and she was almost sure he noted this.

'What then?'

'I was just thinking how delightful it would have been to paddle in that stream we passed,' she answered quietly.

His long-fingered brown hands tightened on the wheel, but he made no comment. His hands were very attractive, she thought, her artist's eye appreciating their length and shape. They were slender without being thin, the bones smooth beneath brown flesh. She wondered if they were hard hands; she felt sure they must be. In spite of the fact that they must have done very little actual hard work, they nevertheless possessed a certain strength and toughness evident in the bones of his knuckles. She would have liked to have touched them, to have felt their texture and shape for herself, to have painted them...

She drew herself up sharply. There was no question of her being allowed to paint any part of the Marquês de Mendao, and in any case, why should she want to do so? She glanced round at her husband sleeping peacefully in the back of the limousine. It was just as well he was unaware of her foolish thoughts.

She settled lower in her seat, lifting the weight of her hair off her neck with a careless hand. Again her action drew the attention of Luis Martinez, and he said: 'As your husband appears to be sleeping at present, perhaps this would be a good moment for me to make certain things clear to you.'

Rachel stiffened. 'What things?'

'First of all, I would prefer that you remember to add the word *senhor* to the statements you address to me.' Rachel gasped, but he went on: 'This is not something that is of a great deal of importance to me, *senhora*, but my mother is of the old school of Portuguese who expect a certain standard of behaviour. Also, it is more fitting that our acquaintanceship should be seen to be on a formal footing, do you not agree?'

'I thought your mother was English—*senhor*.'

Rachel just remembered the suffix.

'She was—she *is*, of course, although lately she has taken Portuguese citizenship. Nevertheless, the customs of my country have always been her customs.'

'I see.' Rachel's tone was dry.

'Secondly, your—appearance, *senhora*.'

'My appearance?' Rachel looked at him in astonishment.

'*Sim, senhora*, your appearance. It is obvious that you do not pay a great deal of attention to the manner of your clothing, but in Portugal women do not wear slacks except on very rare occasions. They adhere to certain principles. A simple dress or perhaps a blouse and skirt are considered much more suitable—can you appreciate this, *senhora*?'

Rachel felt angry. It had not been her wish to come to Portugal, and now this man was daring to criticise her manners and her clothes. Just who did he think he was?

Controlling the tremor in her voice, she said: 'I'm afraid I disagree—*senhor*. For me, trousers are the most comfortable thing in my wardrobe.'

His dark eyes encountered hers and there was unconcealed anger in their depths. His lips were drawn into a line of disapproval and she thought that even in anger he was the most disturbingly attractive man she had ever seen. He was not handsome; it would be an insult to use so paltry a term to describe the carved lines of his tanned features, the high cheekbones, the deepset eyes, that mouth, the lower lip of which when it was not drawn tight as now portrayed an almost sensual fullness. The whiteness of his shirt lay against the brown column of his throat, brushed by the straight black thickness of his hair. What woman, she thought, could not be aware of him as a man, of his extreme masculinity, even if she was married?

Now he looked back at the road, and said: 'Do I take it you intend to oppose me, *senhora*?'

Rachel sighed, her own anger evaporating under other, more disruptive, influences. 'I don't intend any disrespect, *senhor*,' she answered carefully, 'but in the matter of my clothes, I consider I am the best judge of what or what not to wear.'

'I see.' His tone was chilling. 'Perhaps I have approached this wrongly. Perhaps I should have mentioned the matter to your husband first and allowed him to broach it with you.'

Rachel's face burned. 'Is that a threat or a promise, *senhor*?'

His eyes narrowed. 'What do you mean?'

'Surely it must have become apparent to you, *senhor*, that I am an—obedient wife?'

The dark eyes were enigmatic. 'You do not wish me to mention this matter to your husband?'

'Do my wishes matter—*senhor*?' Belatedly she remembered to add the word.

His brows drew together in a frown. 'I am afraid I do not comprehend your meaning, *senhora*.'

'For once we agree. You do not.' Rachel pressed her lips tightly together to prevent them from trembling, realising that this time she had forgotten to use his title altogether.

He expelled his breath through his nostrils. 'Tell me what you think of Mendao,' he said, changing the subject so unexpectedly and so completely that for a moment she was startled. 'This is the valley where our village is situated, the valley of the Rio Meigo.'

Rachel forced herself to pay attention to her surroundings. They were descending into the valley through tree-clad slopes where the scent of pine was strongest. There were more vines, the sound of running water heralding the appearance of the broad but shallow waters of the Meigo which gurgled its way through orchards of cork trees.

Nearer the village, cottages came into view, colour-washed dwellings that while looking picturesque could not, Rachel felt, be very comfortable. They passed black-clad peasant women leading donkeys on which were laden baskets of fruit and vegetables, and children stopped what they were doing to watch them pass.

Many people saluted the car as they passed and Luis Martinez raised a casual hand in acknowledgement of their greeting. Rachel looked at him with sudden perception, beginning to appreciate his concern for formality. Here he was well known, the Marquês de Mendao, and while in England that might mean little or nothing, in his own country, in this valley where no doubt his family had been masters for generations, he was the *Senhor*, the *Patrao*, arbiter of their fates.

'It's very beautiful,' she said at last. 'But of course you know that. Do you own all this land, *senhor?*'

Luis shrugged. 'The land belongs to all of us. We work for it, we till the soil and sow the crops, we gather the harvest; but no man can pronounce himself the owner of something that is the means of livelihood for so many people. The days of slavery are abolished, *senhora*. These people are free. Here in Mendao all men are treated as equals.'

Rachel considered this carefully. 'Nevertheless, it's obvious that you are regarded with—a certain deference. Surely you're not saying that you compare yourself with these peasants!'

The hands on the wheel tightened perceptibly. 'In my country, respect is given to the man, not to the property he calls himself master of.'

Rachel raised her eyebrows. 'Surely that's rather a radical viewpoint for someone with such conservative ideas.'

He frowned. 'We are talking at cross purposes, *senhora*. You think because my ideas of correctness and dignity seem old-fashioned to you that I must be backward-looking.' He shook his head. 'I assure you I am not. The system we have here will bear comparison with any system anywhere in the world and my people are given every opportunity to succeed.'

Rachel was looking at the village. It was quaint and somewhat unworldly to her eyes, but charming nonetheless. As well as a small store and a café, there was a school and a church, and the narrow footbridges over the river which divided the two halves of the village were arched and attractive. The road ran along beside the river for some way, shadowed by evergreen oaks and more of the spreading elm trees.

Beyond the village they branched on to a narrower track and presently came to a gate across the road with the word '*Privado*' printed upon it. Rachel cast a questioning glance in Luis's direction, but for the moment he ignored it, sliding out of the car to open the gate before getting in again and driving through. When the gate was closed behind them, he said:

'I know what you are thinking, but that notice is not for the people who live here. They know they will never be turned away from the *quinta*. But we have *turistas* who can be quite a nuisance.'

Rachel had to smile at this. 'Am I so transparent?' she murmured lightly, and he looked at her.

'To me—in this instance, yes,' he said, and then as though realising the sudden intimacy between them he pressed hard on the accelerator and sent the sleek limousine cruising swiftly up the curving sweep of the drive.

Rachel's first glimpse of the Quinta Martinez was through a belt of trees. Thickly foliaged trees and bushes encroached on the drive from both sides, successfully providing a natural screen between the *quinta* and the rest of the valley. It reminded Rachel of the thorn hedge which had grown up around the castle of the Sleeping Beauty in legend, and in fact, the Quinta Martinez did resemble a small castle at that first appraisal.

Nestling among trees, with dozens of small turrets outlined against a backcloth of deep green, it had an unreal quality, a fairy-tale appearance. Mellow stone was warmed by the rays of the sinking sun which winked on the small Gothic windows and gilded the sculptured façade.

Rachel leant forward in her seat, totally absorbed, for the moment oblivious of her surroundings, of her reasons for being there.

Then Luis said: 'You like my home, *senhora*?' and reality asserted itself.

She sank back in her seat. 'Oh, yes, yes. It's—unbelievably beautiful!'

'My father's family have lived here for many generations,' he said. 'Naturally in recent years the *quinta* has been extensively modernised inside, but not sufficiently to dispel its character, I feel.'

The car emerged from the trees and circled a central courtyard to come to rest at the foot of stone steps leading up to the arched entrance to the building. The steps were shallow, leading into the shade of a terrace which seemed to circle the *quinta*. There was a fountain in the courtyard which gave the sound of constant running water and this was the first thing Rachel noticed as she stepped unaided out of the car.

Luis had walked round to assist her with his innate sense of politeness and she looked up at him helplessly as she scrambled out. 'I'm sorry,' she said. 'I'm not used to anyone opening doors for me—*senhor*!'

31

Luis's lips tightened and then he looked up expectantly as an elderly man appeared at the head of the flight of steps.

'Senhor Marquês!' the old man exclaimed warmly. '*Estimo muito ve-lo de novo.*'

'*Boa tarde*, Mario.' Luis smiled, and Rachel looked away from the warmth of that greeting and leant into the car to say:

'Malcolm! Malcolm, we're here. At the *quinta*.'

Her husband opened his eyes reluctantly. 'What's that? What did you say?'

'We've arrived, Malcolm. In Mendao. How do you feel?'

'If you will permit me...'

Luis was behind her with the folding wheelchair which he had taken from the boot of the car. Rachel drew back abruptly, almost cracking her head on the roof of the car as she did so. She was hot and nervous now that they were actually here, and the idea of meeting the old Marquesa was an intimidating one after what Luis Martinez had said.

She contemplated asking whether she might bathe and change before meeting anyone and thoughtfully went over the few clothes she had brought with her in an effort to think of something suitable to wear. But then she gave herself a mental shake. What was she thinking of allowing these people to influence her to such an extent that she was actually considering dressing to suit them? Good lord, she was not an impressionable schoolgirl, was she? She was twenty-two, and a married woman, completely indifferent to any reaction she might have on Luis Martinez's mother.

At Luis's instigation, the man Mario had drawn the wheelchair up the shallow steps and now Luis was lifting Malcolm out of the back of the silver limousine and carrying him up the steps to install him in the canvas seat of the chair. For the journey Malcolm had worn a dark blue tweed suit, and Rachel thought he must be feeling the heat as she was. Draping the jacket of her slack suit over one shoulder and the strap of her suede bag over the other, she mounted the steps after them, trying not to feel like the intruder she was sure she was.

Mario took charge of the wheelchair. Rachel sensed that Malcolm would have preferred her to guide him, but there was little he could say in front of Luis Martinez which would not sound ungrateful and he said nothing as Luis urged them across the terrace and into the coolness of the mosaic-tiled hall.

Rachel looked about her with sharpened interest. Every artistic nerve within her was throbbing with awareness of the magnificence of her surroundings. Carved pillars, a sweeping baroque staircase, a shadowed gallery above. There were long silk curtains at the windows the colour of wild roses, while on a marble plinth an enormous bowl of those delicately perfumed flowers provided a splash of scarlet. There were small statuettes of saints in the window recesses, reminding one if any reminder was necessary that this was a truly Catholic household, while to the right and left archways gave glimpses of other exquisitely furnished apartments.

If Rachel had imagined that the Marquesa de Mendao would meet them in the hall she was mistaken. On the contrary, at this late hour of the afternoon when the shadows were deepening and a certain coolness was entering the air the *quinta* was as silent as a cloister and only a small dark woman appeared with long black skirts and a white apron who was obviously another of the servants.

She greeted Luis warmly and then looked enquiringly at Rachel and Malcolm. Clearly she had not been expecting two visitors, but her expression was not reproving, merely expectant.

Luis spoke swiftly in his own language, apparently explaining that Senhor Trevellyan had brought his wife with him. Rachel recognised such words as *esposa* and *marido*, but most of what he said was incomprehensible to her.

The woman, whose name was Luisa, eventually nodded and said something in reply which seemed to please her employer, for he nodded, too, and speaking in English, he turned to Rachel and her husband:

'Luisa tells me that she has had a suite prepared for you on the ground floor, *senhor*. In the circumstances we thought it best that you did not have stairs to contend with. It will be a simple matter to prepare one of the adjoining rooms for your wife.'

Malcolm's hands gripped the arms of the wheelchair tightly, revealing his tension, although his expression was complacent as he said: 'I'm sure there's no need to prepare a special room for Rachel. Naturally she will share mine.'

Rachel saw a spasm of something like distaste flicker across Luis's face, and her own cheeks burned suddenly. It was as though Malcolm was speaking deliberately, as if he wanted to shock the other man, but why? What possible reason could he have? Back in England he had been only too eager to agree with everything Luis had said. She could only assume that since arriving in Portugal her husband had known himself home and dry and therefore he had no further need to behave subserviently. This was much more the man she was accustomed to.

'Nevertheless, *senhor*, another room will be prepared,' stated Luis quietly. 'It is possible that your wife might prefer somewhere that she can undeniably call her own as well as sharing your rooms.'

Malcolm made an indifferent gesture. 'Very well.' He looked round. 'Where's Joanna?'

Luis stiffened at the familiarity. 'My mother is no doubt resting, *senhor*. I suggest you allow Luisa to show you to your suite. We can all meet later in the library before dinner.'

'All right.' Malcolm inclined his head and looked round straight into Rachel's face. 'You wheel my chair, Rachel. I prefer you to do so.'

Rachel moved to do as he asked and Luis was forced to stand stiffly aside. But she sensed his silent impatience, his annoyance that in his house a woman should be made to do a man's work when there was a man there capable of doing it. But he made no comment and with a brief bow left them, striding across the hall to take the stairs two at a time.

Luisa led the way down a hall to their left while Mario disappeared outside again to collect their cases. The hall was panelled, inset with narrow windows which overlooked the front courtyard where the fountain played. There were portraits on the opposite wall, grim-looking images of past members of the Martinez family, and Rachel thought how much more attractive the present Marquês was than his predecessors.

Presently Luisa halted before double white doors and throwing them open with a flourish, announced; '*A sala, senhor, senhora.* Is satisfactory?'

Rachel propelled Malcolm's chair into the room looking about her with enjoyment. It was a large drawing room that they had entered, the polished floor strewn with skin rugs, the furniture all pale hide and coolly comfortable. Crossing the room she was able to see an inner courtyard which could be reached by opening long french doors, and she stared with wonder at the tiled patio outside, with its hanging baskets of hydrangeas and geraniums, and attractive striped garden furniture.

Malcolm had said nothing, looking about him without interest, but Rachel could not contain her enthusiasm.

'It's very satisfactory, thank you, Luisa,' she exclaimed. 'I'm sure we shall be very comfortable here.'

Luisa smiled, her teeth very white against the darkness of her skin. 'Is good. See!' She opened another door. 'The bedroom!'

Rachel looked into the next room and saw it was almost as large as the *sala*. A soft cream carpet covered the floor, there were lilac hangings at the windows, while the bedspread was of shades of African violet. Adjoining the bedroom was a bathroom also decorated in lilac and pink. Rachel was quite intoxicated by the beauty of it all.

Malcolm was waiting impatiently in his wheelchair, his fingers drumming on the wooden arms. Mario had arrived with their suitcases, but when Luisa offered to unpack for them, Malcolm was rude.

'There's no need for that,' he snapped ungraciously. 'My wife's quite capable. Besides, I don't want anyone poking around in my things. You can go.'

He dismissed them without a word of thanks and Rachel felt terribly embarrassed. She supposed she ought to be used to her husband's attitude by now, but she was not, and here she had thought he would behave if only to present a façade of geniality.

Luisa and Mario closed the doors behind them and then Malcolm turned on Rachel. 'What the hell do you mean by making eyes at that Portuguese all the way from the airport?' he demanded.

Rachel's lips parted in dismay. 'What?' she murmured faintly.

'Oh, don't pretend you don't know what I mean. Did you honestly imagine I slept all the way here?'

'I—I—naturally I assumed you were tired.' Rachel was too shocked to be retaliatory.

'Well, I wasn't. Not *that* tired, anyway.'

Rachel tried desperately to remember what she and Luis Martinez had spoken about on the journey. Her clothes, of course, but mostly they had argued. There had been no occasion when Malcolm could have imagined that the Marquês de Mendao was aware of her in any other way than that of the wife of a friend of his mother's. Except for that moment at the foot of the drive...

'I think you're the one who's imagining things, Malcolm,' she said carefully, dropping her shoulder bag on to a damask-covered ottoman. 'Senhor Martinez and I spoke very little on the journey from the airport, and as you've seen to it that he regards me with scarcely veiled contempt, I fail to see how you can accuse me of making eyes at him!'

Malcolm stared at her for a long moment. 'But you are attracted to him, aren't you?'

Rachel gasped. 'Of course not.' Her expression hardened. 'I'm not attracted by *any* man!'

Malcolm's face grew ugly. 'Well, see it stays that way. Or by God, I'll find some way to make you pay——'

'Please, Malcolm!' Rachel pressed her arms about her thin body. 'I've told you, you have no need to concern yourself about me.'

A little of the tension left him. 'No. No, I suppose you're right. In any case, a man like Martinez wouldn't look at somebody like you, even without——'

He broke off abruptly and Rachel's eyes narrowed. 'Even without what, Malcolm? Exactly what have you been telling him?'

Malcolm shrugged. 'This and that.'

'How did you explain—our marriage? Surely being

married to someone so much younger than yourself hardly enhances your image.

Malcolm's thin lips quirked. 'There are ways of making the most of every situation,' he replied.

Rachel sighed. It was obvious he had no intention of telling her anything. And in any case, did she want to know? Wasn't it better to remain in ignorance than to hear something which might make her feel even more embarrassed in Luis Martinez's presence?

'Now, get me out of these clothes,' commanded Malcolm, unfastening his tie and the top two buttons of his collar. 'I'm almost roasting alive.'

'What are you going to wear this evening for dinner?' Rachel asked, as she went forward to help him slide his arms out of his jacket.

Malcolm tugged his braces off his shoulders and made an indifferent movement of his head. 'I don't know. I may not join them for dinner. I can always feign tiredness after the journey.'

Rachel took charge of the chair to wheel it into the bedroom. 'You surely don't expect me to join them alone,' she exclaimed.

'No!' He was adamant on that score. 'No, indeed. You'll stay here with me like the dutiful wife you are. I didn't bring you here to Mendao for your amusement, Rachel.'

Rachel stopped the chair beside the bed and came round to face him. 'Exactly why did you bring me, Malcolm?'

Her husband began levering himself forward in the chair and she helped him on to the bed. 'You're my wife, Rachel. I own you, don't forget that. I wasn't going to leave you behind in Mawvry!'

'Why not?'

'I'm not blind, Rachel. I've seen the way men look at you. That Bart Thomas, for example.'

'I'm not interested in the way any man looks at me!'

she declared. 'You should know that.'

'Huh!' Malcolm stared at her impatiently. 'That's what you tell me. But how should I know what goes on inside that head of yours?'

Rachel heaved a sigh and began to help him off with his clothes. 'I shan't leave you, Malcolm. Much as I've been tempted to do. I made a promise, and I'll keep it——'

'Promises! Promises!' Malcolm dragged himself up the bed to relax on the soft pillows. 'I've heard that before. But you're my wife, Rachel, and no one else is going to touch you, do you understand?'

Rachel straightened, hiding the pain in her face. 'No one else would want to,' she said quietly.

'What the hell do you mean?'

Rachel turned away. 'Nothing.'

'Well, you listen to me: where I go, you go, do you hear?'

'Then why didn't you warn me—about coming here?' she cried, turning back to him. 'Why keep it all such a secret?'

Malcolm sniffed, running a hand across the hollow caverns in his throat. 'I didn't want anything to go wrong. I wanted to come here. Joanna owes me that much. If I'd had to tell her about you . . .' He shook his head. 'It would have been difficult, very difficult. Portuguese women aren't like English women. They have a very strict code of ethics. A man of my age marrying an eighteen-year-old girl!' He pointed a finger at Rachel. 'She'd have seen no possible reason for that.'

'But this woman is English! And in any case, how can you now satisfactorily explain it? By telling the truth?' She looked sceptical.

'Joanna has lived so long in Portugal, she's become like them,' said Malcolm, ignoring her questions. 'I saw that four years ago when she came to England. She came for my mother's funeral, both she and Raul.

39

That was her husband, the old Marquês, this man Luis's father. Just like his son, he was. Cold and arrogant, conscious of his own importance!'

Rachel shook her head. 'That still doesn't explain——'

'Leave it, Rachel.'

'But why couldn't you tell me?' she sighed frustratedly.

Malcolm considered her thoughtfully. 'If I'd told you what I'd arranged, how would you have reacted? Would you have been prepared to wait for this man to come and discover who you were?'

Rachel saw the logic of this. If she had known in advance she would have had to have written and told them the truth. She wasn't like Malcolm. She couldn't have waited, depending on their indulgence as he had done. And besides, Malcolm might have been afraid she'd run away at a crucial moment. She had wanted to do so many times in the past and he knew it.

She turned away. 'I need a wash,' she said vaguely. 'I think I'll take a shower. You'll be all right, won't you?'

Malcolm closed his eyes. 'I suppose so.' He opened them again. 'And no disappearing if I fall asleep.'

'Where would I disappear to?' she exclaimed defensively.

'I don't know. But don't, anyway.'

Rachel picked up one of the suitcases and flicked it open. Inside she found some clean underclothing and a towel. Leaving the bedroom, she entered the luxurious surroundings of the bathroom and although there was no need to do so, she locked the door. Then she turned on the shower and began stripping off her clothes. Her brain felt thick and fuzzy, and she was finding it hard to assimilate all this. It was too much in twenty-four hours, and she gave up the will to think...

CHAPTER THREE

WHEN she returned to the bedroom some twenty minutes later and spoke to her husband there was no answer. From the heaviness of his breathing he was obviously asleep, and she tiptoed through to the *sala* and closed the door behind her.

She felt somewhat brighter now and infinitely fresher. She had cooled the water of the shower as she had stood under it, so that her flesh still tingled from that contact and her blood had cooled.

It was almost dark and someone had lit lamps on the patio outside. In the fading light all manner of moths and flying insects came to dance with death around the flames to fall with singed wings upon the mosaic tiling below.

Rachel put on a tall standard lamp with an exquisitely embroidered shade that shed mellow light over the room, and then stretched her length on one of the soft hide couches. It was early yet and she knew that dinner here was served much later. Besides, no doubt she and Malcolm would eat here in the suite.

But with the relaxation came time to think and she wondered with a sense of despair exactly what Malcolm had said to Luis Martinez to explain his marriage to her. She believed what Malcolm had said earlier. To these people such a marriage would need some explaining. He could not possibly have told the truth.

She sighed. What was the truth? Did she know any more? Or had her mind rejected everything connected with this unholy alliance? If this state of affairs here, this unexpected removal to Mendao had changed her life overnight, how much greater had the change been three years ago when she married Malcolm Trevellyan?

She had lived in Mawvry for most of her life. She had moved there with her father when her mother had died and Rachel herself had been only seven years old.

Her father had been an artist, too. Until her mother's death he had made a pretence at earning a living for her sake, but after she was dead he had seen the opportunity to remove himself and his daughter from the tiny house in Bloomsbury which he had owned, to an even tinier cottage in the Cornish fishing village of Mawvry.

Rachel had loved it. She had her father's appreciation of beautiful things, and Mawvry was beautiful. Her father had indulged his passion for painting and sculpture, buying a small fishing boat to supplement his income during the summer months by taking tourists out for pleasure trips around the bay. They had lived simply and Rachel had never considered to wonder how her father managed to support them.

Occasionally in the summer, he would sell a painting and then he would buy steaks and wine and he and Rachel would have a feast. But mostly they lived more modestly, with Rachel learning to cook and sew and care for them both.

Malcolm Trevellyan had always lived in Mawvry. His house was visible on the cliffs above the bay, and Rachel had soon learned that he was not liked among the villagers. He owned property in Mawvry, cottages which he rented to the fishermen and their families, but he was not a good landlord. He loathed spending money, and the roofs of his cottages leaked during the winter months, making them damp and unhealthy.

Fortunately, or so Rachel had always thought, her father had been able to buy their cottage so in that respect they had no dealings with Malcolm Trevellyan. She had never cared for the man. Ever since she was about fourteen, he had gone out of his way to speak to her, but she had not liked the predatory look in his eyes. Of course, she had not understood then why he should look at her in such a way.

Now she shivered and pressed the palms of her hands against the soft leather. If only her father had confided his difficulties to her, allowed her to get a job in one of the towns close by, instead of permitting her to spend her days painting, assuring her that they had no money worries.

When the crisis had come, inevitably Malcolm Trevellyan had been at the core of it. Unknown to her, he had bought their cottage several years earlier when her father needed money. Then, later, he had loaned her father more money, making no demands for payment, pretending to be his friend.

When Rachel was eighteen, his motives had become clear. He had asked her to marry him, and when she had almost laughingly refused, half imagining he could not be serious, he had given her father an ultimatum: persuade Rachel to do as he asked or he would ruin him.

Her father had been desperate. He could not believe that a man he had supposed to be his friend should turn on him in this way. Rachel herself had been distrait. She could see her father failing daily, unable to do anything to help himself. None of the villagers could help them. No one was wealthy enough to pay her father's debts.

Rachel had inevitably come to a decision. She had no other alternative. She went to Malcolm Trevellyan and agreed his terms.

Her father had begged her not to do it. He had assured her he would get the money somehow. He would take the boat out. He would start fishing for himself. These were good fishing waters. He would succeed.

But Rachel knew he would not, and she and Malcolm Trevellyan were married a few days later.

There began for Rachel the most terrible few months of her life. Adding to her anxiety for her father was her own revulsion for the man who had made himself her husband, and she submitted to his demands on her with a despairing humility.

To her father she pretended that everything was turning out all right, but he was not deceived. He saw her change from a glowing creature of warmth and vitality into a slender wraith of pale cheeks and hollow eyes.

He blamed himself, and he could not stand it for very long. Six months later he took out the fishing boat and never returned. A verdict of accidental death was reached, but Rachel knew her father's death had been no accident.

It was as though the whole bottom had dropped out of her world and she had had a nervous breakdown.

It took many months for her to recover. To give him his due, Malcolm secured the very best attention for her, but his motives were not wholly altruistic. He wanted his wife again in every sense of the word, but nevertheless, during that period, she grew to rely on him to a certain extent.

By the time she was fully recovered, any thoughts she might have had of leaving him, of trying to get a divorce, had become distant and unreal, and she hardly needed his reminder that he still possessed her father's promissory notes and would use them if she tried to thwart him.

Instead, she started to paint again, drowning the inadequacies of her life in her art, creating pictures which occasionally brought her money. What small

44

amounts she did earn this way proved sufficient to buy the personal necessities she needed without having to ask Malcolm for every penny, for he seemed to grow meaner as time went by.

And then, just before Christmas last year, he had had a thrombosis. It had been a comparatively mild affair which had left him weakened but active. Although she urged him to take care, he seemed to imagine he was immune after recovering from the first attack so easily, but eventually, two months ago, he had had the second stroke, and it had paralysed him initially all down one side and made the movement of his legs impossible. With therapy, he had regained much of the use of his left hand and arm, but his legs remained helpless.

In consequence, he had become totally unreasonable, demanding Rachel's company at all hours of the day and night. Her occasional visits to the village for shopping or to see her friends were curtailed by the use of the telephone, and he became insanely jealous of anyone, male or female, who spent any time alone with her.

Yet in spite of that, she had never even suspected that he might be planning to leave for Portugal.

She knew of his correspondence with someone in Portugal, of course. From time to time he would give her a letter to post, and now and then there was a reply for him with a foreign postmark. But that was all. He had not troubled to explain to her his association with the Marquesa de Mendao, and certainly Rachel had known nothing of the fact that once Malcolm's family had cared for the young girl who had grown up to marry the wealthy Portuguese nobleman.

But now they were here, in this magnificent *quinta*, the house of the Martinez family, and if she had imagined that this was going to mean more freedom for her, she was mistaken.

She must have fallen asleep because she was awakened by a tapping at the door of the *sala*. She swung her legs to the floor and sat up abruptly, her heart thumping. Immediately, she was conscious of the fact that she had not changed, that she was still wearing the cream slacks and cream cotton ribbed jumper she had worn to travel in.

'Yes?' she called tentatively, and the door opened to admit a young maid.

'Senhora Trevellyan?' she queried, and at Rachel's nod of assent, went on: 'The Senhora Marquesa would like to meet you, *senhora*.'

'Me!' exclaimed Rachel, ungrammatically, getting jerkily to her feet. 'Are you sure you don't mean my husband?'

'*Sim, senhora*. The Senhora Marquesa will come and see Senhor Trevellyan later.'

'But—but——' Rachel looked about her desperately. 'My husband was sleeping a little while ago. He may be awake now. I—I can't leave him—alone.'

The girl glanced behind her and made a summoning movement with her fingers and immediately a swarthy young Portuguese appeared from the corridor outside.

'This is Eduardo, *senhora*.' said the girl, with a slight smile. 'He is to be your husband's—er—*criado*?'

Rachel frowned. 'You mean a kind of—manservant?' She made a helpless gesture. Malcolm would not like this.

'*Sim, sim, senhora*,' the girl was nodding gratefully. 'That is the word; manservant, *sim*.'

'But——' Rachel broke off for a moment. 'I usually look after my husband myself.'

The girl looked most disturbed. 'But not in the

46

Quinta Martinez, *senhora!*' she exclaimed. 'The Senhora Marquesa could not permit such a thing.'

Rachel sighed. 'Just a moment.'

She walked quietly to the door to the bedroom and pressing the handle opened it slightly. It was dark now, but in the faint light from outside she could see that Malcolm was still asleep. Perhaps she might go and see the Marquesa and explain, and be back before Malcolm was even aware that she had gone.

Closing the door again, she turned to the two young Portuguese waiting in the *sala*. They were an attractive couple, she saw now that she relaxed sufficiently to notice them, and she thought how in other circumstances what a boon this could have been. To be relieved, even for a few weeks, of the necessity to do everything for Malcolm would have seemed like a real holiday. But she knew also that Malcolm would never agree.

'All right,' she said now. 'I'm ready.'

If the girl thought the English girl's attire unusual, she hid it well, and turning to Eduardo she instructed him to remain in the suite until the *senhora's* return.

The young man smiled and nodded and Rachel flashed him a grateful smile before accompanying the girl from the room. As they again traversed the corridor, she said: 'What's your name?'

'Rosa, *senhora*.'

'Rosa.' Rachel repeated the word. 'What a pretty name!'

'*Obrigada, senhora*.' Rosa seemed pleased at the small compliment.

Lamps had been lit along the wide corridor, and a chandelier illuminated the hall, casting prisms of light on to the fluted woodwork and delicately carved statuary. From the garden came the drifting scents of stocks and honeysuckle, fanned through the windows by a

47

cooling breeze.

Rosa led the way across the hall to a tall, white-panelled door and tapped lightly. A feminine voice called: '*Entre!*' and then Rosa pushed open the door and urged Rachel before her into the room.

'Senhora Trevellyan, Senhora Marquesa,' she announced.

'Thank you, Rosa. You may leave us.'

The voice came from a woman who was standing gracefully on the soft rug before an exquisitely carved fireplace. Small and slender, silver-grey hair immaculately coiffured shaping a face that was smooth and unlined, dressed completely in black to her small ankles, the Marquesa de Mendao was an imposing figure. Another woman, perhaps a little younger than the Marquesa, was seated on a tapestry-covered *chaise-longue* and as Rosa withdrew they both regarded Rachel with what seemed to her to be a rather hostile scrutiny.

Although Rachel had little chance then to take in her surroundings, she had an impression of book-lined walls and long, crimson hangings, rosewood furniture, and polished wooden floors. The whole room had an aura of elegance and good taste, and there was a faint smell of leather and good tobacco.

Then the Marquesa de Mendao was moving towards her, holding out her hand in greeting. 'How do you do, *senhora*,' she said, speaking English and yet managing to sound wholly Portuguese. 'So you are Malcolm's wife. I am pleased to make your acquaintance.'

Rachel shook the Marquesa's hand nervously. She was distinctly tempted to curtsey, so gracious and imperious did the Marquesa seem, but she managed to reply to the greeting calmly and the Marquesa turned back to her companion.

'Allow me to introduce Senhora Ribialto,' she said.

48

'The *senhora* has been with me for many years now. She is my friend, my associate.'

Rachel presumed that Senhora Ribialto performed the duties of a lady-in-waiting. Certainly she was over-shadowed by the personality of the woman who called herself her friend. In a plain dark gown, buttoned to the neck, her hair drawn severely into a chignon on the nape of her neck, she was a colourless individual.

Rachel shook hands with her, too, but she saw the dark eyes of the other woman move with distaste over her slim-fitting trousers. Turning back to the Marquesa, she said, because it was obviously expected of her at this point: 'It's very kind of you to invite—Malcolm—and myself here, Senhora Marquesa. You—you have a beautiful home.'

The Marquesa inclined her head. 'Thank you, *senhora*. And you may call me Dona Joanna as you are Malcolm's wife. Although, of course, we were unaware that Malcolm had a wife until my son informed us some little time ago.'

Rachel felt a wave of colour sweeping up her neck. 'I know——' she was beginning when the Marquesa interrupted her with an eloquent movement of her hand.

'There is no need to attempt to explain, *senhora*. My son has explained everything to me. Nevertheless, I felt it was a good idea that we should become acquainted—should perhaps understand one another before I speak with Malcolm.'

That sounded ominous. Rachel stiffened. But the Marquesa seemed completely at ease.

'Won't you sit down, *senhora?*' she suggested, indicating a damask-covered armchair. 'Perhaps you would care to try a little wine, some of our own wine, grown in the Martinez vineyards. Sara!'

Rachel subsided into the chair, glad to be off legs which had grown decidedly shaky. She was about to refuse anything to drink when the other woman, Sara Ribialto, rose to her feet and crossed the room to a shadowy corner where a cabinet revealed a comprehensive array of bottles.

'What is it to be?' enquired the Marquesa, seating herself opposite Rachel. 'Some sherry? Or perhaps the wine for which Portugal is famous?'

Rachel would have preferred a simple fruit juice, but she knew that to say so would be tantamount to insulting their hospitality. She agreed to try some port, and although it was not really to her taste, she sipped it obediently and complimented the Marquesa on its quality.

'Do you know much about wine, *senhora*?' asked the Marquesa, watching her closely.

'Very little, I'm afraid.'

'I thought as much.' The Marquesa's lips twisted. 'You will not then be aware of the care which must be taken to produce exactly the right kind of grape for each vintage. You will not know that the sun must not be allowed to make the grape too sweet, or that to pick a grape too soon can make it bitter. Wine producing is a very delicately balanced business, handed down from father to son. It can take many years to perfect a wine, did you know this?'

'I'm afraid not, Senhora Marquesa.'

'*Dona* Joanna,' corrected the Marquesa smoothly.

'Very well, then. Dona Joanna,' said Rachel, biting her lip. 'But please—call me Rachel. I'm not used to such formality.'

The Marquesa merely smiled at this and made no comment. Rachel was aware of Sara Ribialto coming to stand behind the Marquesa's chair, like a silent guardian, and she sensed that pretty soon she was to hear the thing she had been brought here to hear.

'Here in the valley,' went on the Marquesa, 'we are

all aware of such things. It is second nature to us to scan the horizon for signs of cloud, to listen with bated breath for the rumbling of a sudden storm which could ruin a crop. It is our way of life. A way of life which must seem entirely alien to you.'

Rachel stroked the rim of her glass. 'Different, yes,' she agreed.

'And just as our way of life is different, *senhora*, we are different.' Rachel noted the studied formality of that word, *senhora*. 'You may say I was born in England and therefore I am English, but after forty years in Mendao I consider myself wholly Portuguese.'

'Yes?' Rachel didn't know what all this was leading up to.

'And because of this, you present a problem, *senhora*.'

'Me!' Rachel pressed a hand to her throat.

'Yes, *senhora*, you! When I invited Malcolm here for a visit, it presented no difficulties. I understood that he was a sick man, invariably confined to his bed, or occasionally a wheelchair; someone whose presence would create no upheaval whatsoever.'

'But I don't see——'

'Let me finish, *senhora*.' The Marquesa's nostrils flared and Rachel felt as though she had been severely reprimanded. 'We were not to know that someone like yourself would accompany him. Someone young, impulsive, perhaps even a little irresponsible, if you will forgive the word——'

'Irresponsible!' Rachel was stung by the Marquesa's tone.

'Please. Allow me to go on. You must agree that you are young, and therefore no doubt you expect to share in the life of the *quinta* to a much greater extent than your—husband would have done had he been alone.'

'What are you trying to say, Senhora Marquesa?'

Rachel was on her feet now, her hands trembling slightly, almost spilling the liquid in her glass.

'If you will permit me, I will tell you.' The Marquesa's lips thinned. 'You see—you are angry already because I suggest that your presence here might upset the household——'

'Upset the household!' Rachel was astounded.

'Of course.' The Marquesa took a deep breath. 'Luis, my son, is to be married soon, in ten weeks to be exact. His betrothed, the Senhorita Amalia Alejento, is a frequent visitor here. It would be an impossible situation if you were present on these occasions.'

Rachel felt hot all over. She might never have had that shower earlier. But also she was chilled inside, chilled by the coldness of this small, but intimidating, woman. 'Are you suggesting that I ought to leave?' she demanded tremulously, putting down her glass, 'because if you are, I should tell you that nothing would suit me more——'

'*No!* No, that is not what my mother is saying!'

The cold, clipped masculine tones fell into the heated air of the library. In that stormy confrontation they had all been unaware of the door opening and of Luis Martinez entering to stand just inside, regarding them bleakly.

The Marquesa turned to him at once, crossing the room to take his arm. 'Oh, Luis!' she exclaimed. 'I am so glad you are here. Perhaps you can explain the situation to Senhora Trevellyan without creating any more unpleasantness.'

Rachel was breathing unsteadily. She suddenly felt exhausted, as if she had just completed a long and gruelling race. She looked at the three faces all staring at her and there was not an atom of warmth or understanding in any of them.

With a little muffled exclamation, she rushed across

the room past them, and out of the door, not even
stopping when Luis Martinez said: 'Senhora!' in
grim, arresting tones. She looked round the dim hall
helplessly, saw a corridor which she thought led back
to Malcolm's suite of rooms and started along it
chokingly, a hand still pressed to the constriction in her
throat.

But almost as she realised that this corridor was not
the one she had been along earlier, footsteps sounded
behind her and seconds later Luis Martinez came
abreast of her and stepped across her path, preventing
her from making further progress even if she had
wanted to. His eyes were not cold now, they were blaz-
ing with his anger, and a ripple of awareness ran up
her spine. For the moment, the hot Latin tempera-
ment of his ancestors had the upper hand, overwhelm-
ing and subduing the cool, English indifference which
he normally displayed.

'Where exactly do you think you are going, senhora?' he enquired peremptorily, and she took a backward step away from the violence that emanated from
him.

'I was trying to find my way back to—to Malcolm.'
She used her husband's name deliberately, assuming a
defiance she was far from feeling. 'Obviously, I've
taken the wrong corridor.'

'The quinta is a large place, senhora,' he snapped.
'It would not be difficult to get lost in its corridors.'

Rachel's nerves were taut, but she could not let it
go. 'And is that what your mother was trying to tell
me, senhor?' she asked, with scarcely veiled sarcasm.

His fists clenched and for a brief moment she
thought he intended her actual physical injury. But
then he relaxed, and managed to get control of himself.

'No, that was not what she was trying to say, sen-

53

hora,' he stated, taking a deep breath. 'She was merely endeavouring to explain the difference between entertaining a man who is mostly confined to his bed, and entertaining a young woman who might expect certain privileges.'

'I expect nothing, *senhor*,' she replied, half turning away. 'And now, if you'll excuse me——'

'Wait a moment! I have not yet finished.' His jaw was hard. 'Surely you can see that my mother did not expect Senhor Trevellyan to live, as they put it—*com familia*—as one of the family.'

Rachel stared at him. 'And you think I expect that?' she asked incredulously.

'We do not know yet, *senhora*.' He was calm now.

'Well, I can assure you I don't,' she retorted, unevenly. 'I have no desire to mix with people who consider me their social inferior——'

'It's not a question of that!' For a moment his eyes flashed again.

'Then what is it a question of, *senhor*? My outlook on life? My clothes? Oh, yes, you didn't care for them, did you? On the way here you politely tried to warn me, but foolishly I thought you were exaggerating. Well—I'm convinced now. You are different, totally different, and I don't want to be like you any more than you want to be like me!'

And with that she marched away down the corridor, her head held high, when all the time she felt ridiculously like the child who has just said an unforgivable thing to the headmaster.

Once reason ruled her head again, it was a simple matter to distinguish which corridor from the hall led to Malcolm's apartments, and she hurried along, hoping against hope that Malcolm would still be asleep.

But he was not, he was awake, and Eduardo was looking most concerned when she went into the bed-

54

room and found him trying to reason with her husband in broken English. As soon as Malcolm saw her however, he ignored the Portuguese and shouted angrily: 'Where the hell have you been? I told you not to disappear, damn you!'

Rachel heaved a sigh, wondering whether Eduardo understood what Malcolm was saying. Certainly he understood the other man's tone of voice, and his swarthy face was anxious.

'The Senhora Marquesa sent for me,' she replied quietly. 'Would you have had me refuse to go?'

'Why couldn't she come here?' Malcolm was aggressive.

'I think she's going to. But you were asleep, and I suppose she thought it would be a good opportunity to—to speak to me.'

'What did she say?'

Rachel sighed and glanced at Eduardo. 'This and that.' She linked her hands together. 'You can go, Eduardo. And will you tell whoever is responsible that Senhor Trevellyan and I will eat in our rooms?'

'*Sim, senhora.*' It was obvious that Eduardo understood more English than he spoke. With an awkward bow in Malcolm's direction he went out of the room and presently Rachel heard the outer door close behind him.

'What did you do that for?' asked Malcolm, unpleasantly. 'You don't know what arrangements have been made about us taking our meals.'

Didn't she? Rachel's mouth felt suddenly dry, but she refrained from mentioning it. Instead, she said: 'How do you feel?'

Malcolm heaved an impatient sigh. 'I'm all right,' he muttered. 'I just want to know what Joanna said to you. Did she mention me?'

Rachel ran her tongue over her upper lip. 'Not—not

really. I think it was me she wanted to look over.'

Malcolm looked belligerent. 'Why?'

'Oh, you know.' Rachel turned away, picking up his shoes and placing them neatly under the end of his bed. 'Curiosity, I guess.' There was no point in angering him still further with the Marquesa's real reasons. Things were going to be difficult enough here without Malcolm's involvement in the affair. All the same, she wished Malcolm were the kind of man she could tell, someone with a sense of pride who would refuse to stay here under such circumstances. But then, she thought dryly, had Malcolm been that kind of a man this situation would never have happened.

'Well?' he said now. 'So what happened?'

'Very little. We—we drank some wine, and—and she explained that her son is getting married in a few weeks' time and that naturally, not knowing that I was coming with you, she was going to have little time to spare to entertain me.'

Malcolm hunched his shoulders. 'That's just as well, isn't it?' he grunted. 'I don't want you disappearing every minute of the day when I might need you.'

Rachel turned. 'That young man who was here just now—Eduardo—he—he was sent to help you. I—I believe the Marquesa would like you to accept him as your manservant while you're here.'

Malcolm's expression darkened. 'I don't need any *man*-servant.'

'Why not?' Rachel spread her hands. 'Aren't I entitled to a holiday, too? I shall be here, if you want me. It's just that—well—it would make things easier.'

'I'll bet it would.' Malcolm tugged viciously at the bedspread. 'And how do you think I'd feel submitting to the ministrations of a stranger?'

'You did that when you were in hospital.'

'That was different. They were nurses, trained nurses. Eduardo! Pah!'

The subject was dropped. Malcolm wanted Rachel to help him get ready for the Marquesa's visit. She helped him into the wheelchair and guided him into the bathroom. The delightful accoutrements of this apartment made no apparent impression on him. They were purely functional requirements so far as he was concerned.

Back in the bedroom he decided to put on his pyjamas and receive the Marquesa in the bedroom itself. It was easier and infinitely more comfortable for him to put on a pair of cotton pyjamas than a heavy suit, and besides, it created the impression that he wanted to create.

She came just before their dinner was to be served, arriving at the suite in the company of Sara Ribialto and her son. To Rachel, it smacked of a royal visit, and after taking one look at Luis Martinez's dark face she left them, unable to listen to Joanna Martinez without feeling a decided sense of distaste.

She waited in the *sala*, pacing about restlessly, and when Luisa, the housekeeper, appeared to tell her that her room was prepared, she went with her gladly, eager to escape from the murmur of their voices in the other room.

She had been given a small sitting room, bedroom and bathroom for her own use. They were a little further along the corridor than Malcolm's rooms and opened on to the same inner patio. Designed in shades of turquoise and apple green they were beautifully cool-looking, and a little of her earlier enthusiasm came back.

'You like, *senhora*?' Luisa was anxious.

'I like very much,' Rachel replied, swinging round on her heels. 'Very much indeed.'

'That is good. The Senhor Marquês, he say you need

more than just bedroom.'

Rachel stopped her spinning. 'The Marquês told you to prepare these rooms for me?'

'*Sim, senhora.*' Luisa folded her hands.

'You mean—you would just have prepared a bedroom?' Rachel spoke slowly.

'*Sim, senhora.* There are other rooms—how do you say it—near—*next* to your husband's.'

'Part of the suite, you mean?'

'Is correct, *senhora.*'

'I see.'

Rachel's palms felt suddenly moist. Now why had he done this? How much easier it would have been for him to have directed Luisa simply to make up a bedroom adjacent to Malcolm's, and yet he had instructed her to take the trouble to make ready a whole suite! And this from a man to whom she had spoken so rudely perhaps little more than a half hour ago.

'Did—did the Marquês give any reason why I should be given a suite of my own?' she asked, unable to prevent the question.

'*Sim, senhora.* The Senhor Marquês, he say you paint pictures; that you need room to work.'

'He said that?' Rachel was astounded. She wasn't even aware that Luis Martinez knew she painted. Malcolm must have told him. But that was surprising because Malcolm did not really care for this occupation. She became too detached when she was working, too remote, and jealousy prevented him from seeing any merit in the pictures she completed. And in any case, he had refused to allow her to bring any of her painting equipment with her to Portugal.

Luisa was clearly waiting to be dismissed and with a smile Rachel complied. But after the housekeeper had left her, her thoughts continued to surge chaotically. What might Malcolm's reaction to her being given her own suite of rooms be? He would surely not be enamoured of the idea. It might be easier to allow him to assume that she had merely been provided with somewhere to sleep and leave it at that.

But she knew she would have to tell him. It was not in her nature to be secretive, and besides, what harm was there in her having somewhere to call her own?

She returned to Malcolm's suite to find that the Marquesa and her son had left, and Rachel went tentatively to the bedroom door, expecting another argument with Malcolm over her second disappearance.

However, a trolley containing their dinner had been wheeled into the bedroom and Eduardo was in the process of serving it. When Rachel appeared, Malcolm regarded her broodingly, but he was clearly not angry as he had been before.

'Where were you?' he demanded, as she entered the room nervously.

'I went with Luisa. She showed me my rooms.'

'Rooms?' Malcolm frowned, picking up the plural immediately.

'That's right. I've been given a sitting room, too.'

Malcolm's mouth twisted. 'You won't need it.'

'I might.' Rachel cast an awkward glance in Eduardo's direction wondering how much of this the young Portuguese understood. 'You apparently told the Marquês that I painted. He's given me an extra room for that purpose. I imagine he thinks I'll need something to do to fill my time when you're resting.'

Malcolm studied her intently. 'But you haven't brought your equipment with you.'

'I know, I know. But the Marquês may not be aware of it. You shouldn't have told him if you didn't want him to know.'

A strange looked crossed Malcolm's face for a moment and he chose to pounce on Eduardo then, verbally castigating him for daring to drop a tiny speck of sauce on to the spotlessly white napkin he was using. By the time Eduardo had been dismissed, the topic was forgotten and Rachel was relieved. All the same, she wished she had brought her oils and canvas with her. She would have enjoyed working here.

CHAPTER FOUR

RACHEL awakened next morning with a strange feeling of excitement. She couldn't understand it, and she blinked rapidly at the rose-tinted sculptures on the ceiling above her bed, wondering with a sense of expectancy exactly where she was. When she moved her legs, they encountered nothing but cool silk, and when she looked towards the foot of the bed she saw pale turquoise drapes moving in a faint breeze by the windows. There were shutters on the windows which she had closed the night before, and bright sunlight was slatting through them.

She sat up abruptly, the thick mass of her hair tumbling in confusion about her bare shoulders. Of course—she was in Mendao; in the Quinta Martinez; and what was more, this was her suite, her bedroom, her enormous bed!

Grasping a handful of silk sheet, she cupped her chin on her fists. She had not expected to be allowed to sleep here alone, but after taking his tablets last evening, Malcolm had been tired, and in that drowsy state he had not cared where she slept. Indeed, since his illness they had slept apart, but after what he had said to Luis Martinez yesterday she had expected to be forced to share his bed.

So she had come here, to her own suite, and after taking another cooling shower she had slipped between the sheets without bothering to don the nylon nightdress she had brought with her. There had been something exciting and sensual about sleeping unclothed, and this morning it was as though a little of that excitement had spilled over to infect the day.

After all, in spite of the Marquesa's remarks, in spite of Malcolm's jealousy and irascibility, things looked so much brighter under the heat of the sun, and she could look forward to days of relaxing and sunbathing without any of the menial household tasks to trouble her.

Unwillingly, thoughts of Luis Martinez, Marquês de Mendao, came to her mind. At some time she would have to thank him for all this, and perhaps apologise for her behaviour of the previous evening. But she didn't want to think about him just now. He unsettled her, he made her feel nervous and restless, and she hoped his fiancée, the unknown Amalia Alejento, would be around to fill his time to the exclusion of everything and everyone else.

She sighed, her oval face troubled. It was strange how that name, Amalia Alejento, had stuck in her mind. She didn't know the girl, she didn't even expect to get to know her. And yet it seemed that everything remotely connected with Luis Martinez remained annoyingly in the forefront of her mind.

Thrusting all thoughts aside, she slid out of bed and then pulled on a quilted housecoat before approaching the shutters of the windows. Pulling them open, she leant on the sill breathing deeply.

Outside in the patio, a glass-topped table had been laid for breakfast, but just for two. A gardener was watering the hanging plants and those that grew in such profusion in tubs set here and there, and beyond a belt of almond trees, presently thick with pink and white blossom, the lushness of the gardens could be seen. Rachel had never seen such a variety of flowering plants and shrubs, their scents proving intoxicating even at this early hour. For it was early, a glance at her watch had told her that; barely six-forty-five. There were scarlet glimpses of poinsettia and hibiscus, soft magnolias and white oleanders, all tumbling in profusion over stone walls and trellises, with exotically patterned butterflies adding a somnolent kind of humming sound to the already drowsy air.

The gardener had finished his duties and disappeared, and on impulse Rachel went into her bathroom and after showering and cleaning her teeth, she quickly put on her clothes.

The night before she had brought the suitcase containing most of her things into this bedroom, and now she rummaged through her belongings and came up with a shabby pair of cotton jeans and a sleeveless orange sweater with a low round neck. She brushed her hair until it was thick and smooth, loose about her shoulders. It would have been cooler to put it up, she reflected, but she didn't want to waste any more of these few moments of freedom.

Emerging into her sitting room, she saw that as in Malcolm's sitting room long french doors opened on to the inner patio. Pushing open these doors, she stepped outside and stood in the shadow of the balcony above, stretching with delicious abandon. Then she looked about her with interest.

Clearly this inner patio was not the central point of the *quinta*. No doubt there were other inner courtyards like this, and probably these rooms had been chosen for them because they were self-contained and apart from the rest of the household. Her mouth twisted wryly. Oh, well, what of it? She didn't want to mix with the Marquesa and her friends anyway!

The glass-topped table was set partly in the shade of the balcony, and she walked towards it, silent on her sandal-clad feet, running her fingers over its smooth cold surface. She looked towards the almond trees. She would like to see what was beyond. It was very early. Dare she take a walk? What harm could it do? Malcolm wouldn't be awake for hours yet.

With an impulsive little movement of her shoulders, she started off across the courtyard. The sun was warm upon her shoulders and she rested one hand on top of her head, feeling the intense heat.

Beyond the almond trees was a stretch of green turf, and beyond this was a rose garden. Rachel loved roses, and she strolled across the grass towards them. There was no one about, she might have been alone in the *quinta*, and she wandered into a small arbour fragrant with the scents of the gorgeous blooms. Surely they would all have won prizes at some garden show back home, she thought, tempted to finger the velvet-soft petals.

The sound of running water brought her to another arbour where there was a fountain and a stone mermaid who drank constantly from an opened oyster shell in her hands. It was a curiously real sculpture, and Rachel went down on her haunches beside it, trailing her fingers in the coolness. She almost jumped out of her skin when an unmistakably attractive masculine voice, said: '*Bom dia, senhora.* I trust you slept well.'

Rachel scrambled hastily to her feet, immediately conscious of her shabby jeans and thin ribbed sweater which showed such an expanse of her smooth throat. Although Luis Martinez was wearing casual clothes, his close-fitting cream trousers and navy knitted cotton shirt were immaculate, the lacing at the neck of the shirt not revealing so much as an inch of his chest. The short sleeves showed his muscular forearms, liberally covered with dark hairs, a gold watch, on a plain leather strap, glinting.

'Thank you, I slept very well—*senhor*,' she replied, brushing her palms down the sides of her jeans to dry them. 'It—it was kind of you to provide me with—

with a suite to myself.'

Luis's fine dark eyes were intent. 'Which you—used, of course.'

'Yes, *senhor*.' Rachel felt vaguely embarrassed by his directness. 'And—and while I have the opportunity, I—I should apologise for what I said yesterday evening. It—it was very rude of me, and I regret it.'

'Do you?' His eyes challenged hers. 'What do you regret?'

She sighed. 'It's better that we don't become involved in arguments of that sort,' she answered. 'I—I've just been admiring your roses. They're magnificent, aren't they?' She glanced round a little desperately. 'I—am I trespassing?'

He studied her for a long disturbing minute, and then he frowned and ignoring her question said: 'Do you think you will do much work while you are here, *senhora*?'

'Work?' Rachel frowned. 'What kind of work?'

'I understand from your husband that you are an artist, *senhora*.' His eyes narrowed. 'Is this not so?'

'Oh! Oh, I see.' Rachel nodded. 'Yes, yes, it's so. I do paint a little. Not very well, I'm afraid, but I make a little money at it.'

'Well?' There was impatience in his voice now. 'And do you think you will do much work while you are here? I would hazard to guess that you will find few more idyllically suitable places to paint.'

Rachel bent her head. 'I'm afraid I won't be able to, *senhor*. I—I haven't brought my equipment with me.'

He frowned. 'Why not?'

'I—I didn't think of it,' she lied, unable to tell him what Malcolm had said.

Luis folded his arms. 'I suppose you did have a lot to arrange in an extremely short time,' he agreed. 'It is conceivable that you might forget. And yet...' He shrugged. 'So how do you expect to fill your days, *senhora*?'

Rachel moved uncomfortably. 'I expect I shall find plenty to do. I read, too, you know, and sometimes I read to Malcolm. Then there's the sun...' She made an involuntary gesture towards the gleaming ball of gold above them. 'You don't have to concern yourself about me, *senhor*.' A smile tugged at the corners of her mouth suddenly. *As if he would!*

'Something is amusing you, *senhora*?'

His face was suddenly grim and she sobered instantly. 'Not really, no,' she denied, turning away. 'I'd better be going back...'

He glanced at his watch. 'It is only a little after seven-thirty, *senhora*. Breakfast will not be served before eight. Come, I will show you something more of the *quinta*.'

Rachel drew an unsteady breath. It was the very last thing she had expected him to say. 'Perhaps some other time, *senhor*,' she ventured unhappily.

'Why not now?' His tone brooked no argument and there was an arrogant tilt to his head.

Rachel looked down at her sweater and jeans. 'I don't think your mother would approve, *senhor*,' she began awkwardly.

'I am not a child, *senhora*. I do not need permission to do something I choose to do. Do I take it that you do not wish to accompany me? That you are merely using my mother as an excuse?'

'Not at all...'

Rachel stared at him helplessly, aware that she wanted to go with him very much. But that very desire was sufficient to still her acceptance at birth.

Since her marriage to Malcolm she had had little to do with any other man. She had had little wish to associate with members of the opposite sex. Her experi-

66

ences with Malcolm had left their mark on her, and in spite of her youthful appearance, she was not the inexperienced teenager she seemed, eager to sample the delights of every forbidden interlude that came her way.

On the contrary, until now she had never felt a physical attraction towards anyone. The physical side of her marriage to Malcolm she had found so repugnant to everything that was artistic in her nature that she had come to the conclusion that she must be frigid, and that was why she found this desire to spend time in Luis Martinez's company so unexpected and so disturbing. She didn't want to feel attracted to anyone, least of all someone like him, and she realised her most sensible course of action would be to avoid him after this.

Luis was unaware of her mental upheaval. He had taken her denial of making excuses as acceptance and was now indicating a path which skirted the stone mermaid in her watery basin and entered a network of trellised walks where the sun was filtered. 'Come,' he said. 'We will go this way, *senhora*.'

Rachel hung back, shaking her head. 'I'm afraid I have to go back, *senhor*,' she said regretfully. 'I—Malcolm might be awake and needing me.'

'Eduardo will attend to your husband, *senhora*.'

'But Malcolm won't allow him to do so.'

Luis's face hardened perceptibly and she felt a momentary sense of loss that she should have been responsible for severing any tenuous relationship there might have been between them.

'Very well, *senhora*.' He made no further effort to detain her. '*Adeus*, for the present!'

Without waiting for her to make any move, he turned and strode swiftly away, and she watched him go with a fast beating heart. Now why on earth had he offered to show *her* the grounds of the *quinta*? Had it been a desire on his part to atone for his own behaviour of the night before, or was it simply that having come upon her as he had he had felt obliged to be polite?

Either way, it didn't much matter. And as she walked back across the lawns to the shadows of the inner patio, she thought that no doubt he was more annoyed at her having turned him down when few people ever did than disappointed that she should find some reason to reject him. She sighed. What a situation!

Back in her rooms, she found an elastic band and secured her hair with it before going out into the corridor and along to Malcolm's suite. To her surprise, the young manservant, Eduardo, was already there in the *sala*, changing the flowers in the wide bowls which graced every available shelf and table top.

He straightened at her entrance and bowing slightly, said: '*Bom dia, senhora.*'

'*Bom dia,* Eduardo.' Rachel said her first Portuguese words rather tentatively. 'Er—is my husband awake?'

'I don't know, *senhora*. I have come now to change the flowers.'

Rachel nodded. 'You mean you've just arrived?'

Eduardo smiled. '*Sim, senhora. Agora mesmo!*'

Rachel wasn't quite sure what that meant, but she smiled, too, and went lightly to the bedroom door. Inside, in the shadowy interior, she could just see Malcolm stirring in the huge bed. Taking a deep breath, she pushed wide the door and entered the room.

'Good morning,' she greeted him, going to the windows to open the shutters. 'Did you sleep well? It's a glorious morning.'

Malcolm came round slowly, coughing a little as he struggled up on his pillows. 'What time is it?' he grunted.

Rachel looked at her watch. 'A little after eight. But already the sun's very high.'

Eduardo came to the bedroom door. '*Bom dia, senhor!*' he saluted him, with apparent disregard for the way he had been dismissed the night before. 'Would you like me to help you to dress?'

Malcolm's face glowered. 'I don't need your help,' he retorted. Then he looked at Rachel. 'You can help me to the bathroom. But I'm not getting dressed.'

'But you must!' Rachel's voice was filled with dismay. 'Our breakfast table has been laid outside, on the patio. Oh, Malcolm, do get dressed and I can wheel your chair outside and we can have breakfast together.'

'I don't want to sit outside.' Malcolm was apparently in an obstructive mood. 'It's too damn hot already.' He pushed off the bedcovers, and then realised Eduardo was still standing there. 'And send him away! I've told you, I don't want anyone else fussing me.'

Rachel sighed. She looked towards Eduardo regretfully. 'I'm sorry, Eduardo,' she said. 'But apparently your services won't be needed.'

Eduardo hesitated for a moment and then seeing Malcolm's grim determination he made an eloquent little movement of his hands and left them.

By the time Rachel had assisted Malcolm into the wheelchair, taken him to the bathroom and brought him back again, and then helped him on to the bed, she was streaming with perspiration. Although he was thin now, his bones were large and heavy, much too heavy for someone as slight as herself, but Malcolm never showed her any consideration. He levered himself back on to the pillows and then said: 'We'll have breakfast now.'

Rachel sighed, fanning herself with one hand. 'Couldn't we sit outside?' she appealed. 'In the shade of the balcony? It's so much more refreshing out there than in this stale air you've been breathing all night long.'

Malcolm ignored her, reaching for the paperback thriller he had brought with him for the journey and which as yet was unread. 'Go and ring for breakfast or whatever else you do around here to get service,' he remarked, and she was forced to comply.

If Eduardo thought it strange that Rachel should not enjoy the experience of having breakfast outside on the patio and chose to eat inside instead with her husband he managed to disguise it. Perhaps after his own experiences at Malcolm Trevellyan's hands he was beginning to appreciate how much easier it was to placate him, and as the windows stood wide to the air and the warm rolls and conserve and strong black coffee were delicious, Rachel managed to forget her own disappointment.

After breakfast was over, she unpacked the remainder of Malcolm's belongings from his suitcase and hung them away in the capacious wardrobes that lined the walls. Then she washed her own underclothes in the bathroom handbasin, leaving them on the bath to dry, and returned to the bedroom to find Malcolm staring broodingly into space.

'Where did you disappear to last night?' he asked, as she entered the room.

Rachel frowned. 'Disappear? I didn't disappear. I went to bed—in my room next door.'

'Next door?'

'Well—a few doors away, then.'

'I told you I expected you to sleep in here. What if I'd needed you through the night?'

'Malcolm, you know since your illness we've had separate bedrooms. Besides, it was so hot. And if you had needed me you could have done the same here as at home. You could have shouted for me.'

Malcolm hunched his shoulders. 'You'd never hear me in this place.'

'Of course I should. Heavens, even footsteps echo along these corridors.'

Malcolm frowned. 'Have you seen any of the family this morning?'

Rachel hesitated. 'Have you?'

'You know I haven't. Joanna said she'd come along this morning for a chat. We have a lot to say to one another. You can read outside if you want to.'

Rachel was grateful for the predicted dismissal. She had no desire to listen to the Marquesa making small talk with her husband. But she did have something more to say. 'Malcolm,' she began slowly, 'if you're going to stay in your rooms all the time we're here, what point was there in coming? I mean—don't you want to get out in the sunshine? To see all the beauty that's around you?'

'I don't intend to stay in my rooms all the time we're here,' Malcolm retorted calmly. 'On the contrary. I expect Joanna will put a car at our disposal. I shall get out and about, but there's no hurry. We have plenty of time.'

Rachel sighed. What was Malcolm trying to do? Why did his words arouse such a feeling of unease inside her? How long did he intend to stay here?

The Marquesa came just before eleven. This time only Sara Ribialto was with her, soberly dressed as before in a dark gown. Rachel was relieved that Luis was not with them. She felt it was too soon for her to face him again. This morning's confrontation had left her feeling strangely vulnerable and she didn't altogether understand why.

The Marquesa had arranged for coffee to be served to them during the visit and Rosa performed this ser-

71

vice. She brought Rachel's out to the patio and smiled apologetically.

'You do not wish that I should serve yours indoors with the Marquesa and your husband, *senhora*?' she queried in surprise.

'Thank you, no.' Rachel looked up from the magazine she had found in the *sala* and which she had been studying with concentration. 'I'm quite happy here, Rosa.' And it was true. Seated here on the patio, in one of the low basketwork loungers with their pretty flower-splashed cushions, shaded from the sun by the chair's canopy, she was almost content. 'But tell me,' she added, 'is there anywhere I might find a Portuguese phrase book? You know the sort of thing; with words and phrases in English and then Portuguese.'

Rosa frowned, 'There are such books in the library, *senhora*. I have heard that when the Senhora Marquesa first came here she had to learn our language. But I could not get such a book for you without permission, *senhora*.'

'No. No, of course not.' Rachel leant across to pour herself some coffee from the jug which Rosa had placed on the glass surface of the table nearby. There was a jug of cream, too, and Rachel added two heaped spoonsful of sugar for good measure.

Rosa looked anxious. 'You wish me to ask the Senhor Marquês, *senhora*?' she ventured.

Rachel shook her head quickly. 'Oh, no, don't bother. I expect I'll be able to pick one up some time if we're near some shops. Thank you, all the same.'

Rosa smiled, nodded, and departed, and Rachel carried her cup to her lips. The magazine she had been studying was a Portuguese magazine and she had been thinking that learning the language might give her something with which to fill her days. For although it was very pleasant there in the sun, her mind was too active to allow for complete inactivity for very long.

There was the sound of footsteps echoing lightly on the mosaic tiling of the patio and she glanced round expecting to see Rosa returning for the coffee cup. But instead she encountered the Marquesa's grey eyes, which right now had an anxious expression in their depths.

Rachel got to her feet at once, and then chided herself for so doing. Joanna Martinez was not royalty, and just become she acted that way did not mean that Rachel should do likewise. But she was on her feet now and perhaps it was easier to feel on equal terms with the woman when she was not actually looking up to her.

'*Bom dia, senhora.*' The Marquesa was coolly polite. 'I see you are enjoying the sunshine.'

Rachel took her cue from the older woman and nodded. 'Good morning, Senhora Marquesa. And yes, I find it quite delightful out here.'

The Marquesa plucked at her pearls. She seemed nervous, and Rachel wondered what Malcolm had said to create this impression on her. For what else could it be? The Marquesa was not nervous of her.

'These courtyards are part of the older section of the building,' the Marquesa said at last. 'The Moorish influence is strongest here. I imagine quarters like these were used to house the female members of the household—the *seraglio.*'

Rachel tucked her thumbs into the belt of her jeans. 'I didn't realise it was so old.'

'Most of the building isn't. Naturally, much restoration has had to be done, *senhora*. But the character of the building, the influences that created it, they have been maintained.'

'Yes.' Rachel listened with interest.

The Marquesa moved a little nervously. 'My son's

73

fiancée, Senhorita Alejento, is coming this afternoon. I wish you to join us in the main *sala* at four o'clock for afternoon tea.'

Rachel was flabbergasted. After the way the Marquesa had acted the evening before, this invitation was most unexpected. Why should she be invited to meet the Marquês's fiancée? It was nothing to do with her. And besides, the idea of taking tea with two aristocratic women was not at all to her liking.

Then, to her surprise, Malcolm appeared through the wide french doors, being propelled in his wheelchair by Eduardo. The astonishment of seeing him so unexpectedly shocked her into silence.

The Marquesa had heard the swish of tyres too and turned slowly, her expression enigmatic. 'Hello, Malcolm,' she murmured, and Rachel was amazed at the change in her voice. 'I've just been—inviting your wife to our little tea party this afternoon.'

Rachel almost gasped. So Malcolm was to join them in the *sala*! She would never have believed it.

'I'm sure we're both looking forward to meeting your son's fiancée, Joanna,' remarked Malcolm calmly. 'Aren't we, Rachel?'

Rachel didn't know how to reply. The whole situation seemed unreal somehow. Last night the Marquesa had been scarcely civil, obviously unwilling to welcome either of them into the household except in a purely superficial way. They were to be offered the Martinez hospitality, but that was all. And now . . .

'I—I—if you say so, Malcolm,' she murmured awkwardly.

Malcolm frowned. 'Of course, we're looking forward to it, Joanna. Rachel's a little—overawed, that's all.'

Overawed! Yes, Rachel supposed she was. But not in the way Malcolm was implying.

Sara Ribialto had been hovering in the background,

but now she said: 'You won't forget that we have some letters to do before lunch, will you, Dona Joanna?' in rather disapproving tones, as though she at least objected to so much attention being given to these English interlopers.

The Marquesa turned, with relief, Rachel thought. 'Oh, no, Sara, I haven't forgotten. I will come now. You will excuse me?'

Malcolm smiled, 'Of course.'

The Marquesa's lips moved in the semblance of a smile and then she held her head high as she preceded Sara through the french doors.

As soon as she was out of earshot, Malcolm dismissed Eduardo, and looked impatiently towards Rachel. 'Well?' he said. 'Haven't you got anything to say?'

Rachel shook her head in a confused way. 'You've dressed,' was all she could think of.

'That chap Eduardo helped me. Clumsy devil! He almost overturned the wheelchair when I was lowering myself into it. He won't do that again!'

A faint smile touched Rachel's lips. She could imagine the reaction that would have had. She dropped down on to the lounger again, and said: 'So we're to have tea with the family.'

'Why not? I thought we might as well get to know the bride-to-be as we'll probably be invited to the wedding.'

Rachel's lips parted. 'The wedding's ten weeks away. We won't even be here then.'

Malcolm's expression hardened. 'Why won't we?'

'Well——' Rachel looked about her helplessly. 'I mean—how could we be?'

'Why shouldn't we be here? The invitation I was issued had no terminal date upon it.'

'No, but—well, that was different. And they thought you were alone—and lonely. They didn't know you

75

had a wife.'

'So? What of it? You won't be too great a drain on their resources. They can afford it, believe me!'

'That's not the point, Malcolm. We can't just hang on here indefinitely, until someone kicks us out.'

'Why not? I think I'm going to like it here. The food's damn good, and the weather is definitely more reliable. Besides, it's years since I took a holiday. I'd have thought you'd welcome a break from housework.'

Rachel stood up again, unable to sit still suddenly. Malcolm's words had made her worried and restless. She didn't want to sponge upon these people. She had never dreamt when she packed their things a couple of days ago that Malcolm was putting no time limit on their stay. Apart from anything else, she didn't want to feel beholden to them, and nor did she want to be forced to see much more of Luis Martinez...

'Oh, Malcolm,' she pleaded now, 'summer's coming. It will be very hot here. Are you sure you'll be able to stand it? You know how delightful the summer months can be back home. Couldn't we leave after a couple of weeks——'

'Stop talking such drivel!' Malcolm's mouth had turned down at the corners. 'I'll decide when we go home, and that's that.'

Rachel turned away. There was nothing more she could say. Malcolm was her husband, after all, and these were his friends, not hers. If he chose to stay here and be humiliated, what could she do about it?

CHAPTER FIVE

RACHEL dreaded the prospect of taking tea in the main *sala* and despised herself for doing so. Surely she should have more confidence, she told herself severely, as she brushed her hair before returning to Malcolm's suite later that afternoon. What was she? A woman or a mouse? Had she so little sophistication that she considered herself incapable of holding her own with an arrogant old woman and a girl who could surely not be so very different in age from herself?

Since lunch, thoughts like these had buzzed in her brain, preventing her from sleeping even though Malcolm had agreed to rest and given her permission to do likewise.

Lunch had been served late by British standards, but the meal of *sopa de camarao* or creamed shrimps, a fresh green salad and grilled sardines, rounded off by cheese and fruit and more of the strong aromatic continental coffee, had been delicious.

But now it was time to wheel Malcolm along to the main *sala*. Rachel felt nervous. She had scanned the contents of her wardrobe several times already, but although she possessed several simple cotton dresses which she had made herself, she had eventually discarded the idea of wearing one of them.

She had done so for two reasons: firstly because she knew that whatever she wore would be eclipsed by the elegance of the two other women and her clothes would not stand their kind of scrutiny; and secondly she was reluctant to dress in a way which would give Luis Martinez the misguided notion that she had been intimidated by his remarks about what she should wear.

All the same, it took an enormous amount of stamina to stick to her decision to wear trousers, although she did make the concession of changing from sweater and jeans into a long-sleeved cream cotton shirt and pink cotton slacks.

Malcolm was irritable as she propelled his chair along the corridor. His short sleep had been interrupted by the arrival of Eduardo, sent by the Marquesa to assist him to dress. His grey flannels were slightly creased and he had refused to put on a clean shirt, and consequently he was not at his most charming.

They encountered Rosa in the hall, and she hurried forward to knock at the doors of the *sala* for them. At a summons, she threw open the doors and then stood back to allow Rachel to wheel Malcolm's chair into the room.

The main *sala* was immense and imposing as Rachel had expected it to be after having experience of the lesser apartments in the building. Walls with hanging tapestries reached up to a ceiling which was high and curved, inlaid with lapis lazuli. A bronze lamp was suspended above stiff-back chairs and highly polished furniture, small carved tables on which rested glazed bowls and Turkish vases, ewers inlaid with silver and copper, delicately sculpted figures in marble, silver and bronze. It was obvious, even to the most unknowledgeable observer, that these articles were priceless, and Rachel wondered how anyone dared to lift them to dust the winking brightness of the shining surfaces beneath.

There were four people gathered already in the *sala*; the Marquesa and her companion, Sara Ribialto; Luis; and a strange young woman who was clearly

Amalia Alejento. The three women were seated when Rachel and Malcolm entered, with Luis standing slightly behind his fiancée's chair.

Rachel looked at Amalia. She was the most beautiful woman she had ever seen. She was dark, as only a Portuguese is dark, but with a magnolia-white skin and deep limpid eyes. Her rounded figure was shown to advantage by a slim-fitting dress of navy linen with a white Puritan collar that accentuated the curve of her neck. She sat in the high-backed chair, her hands folded in her lap, an expression of benign complacency on her face. No doubt as she grew older her present curves might thicken into plumpness, but that cool hauteur would never change, and she had all the attributes necessary for a future Marquesa de Mendao.

Rosa closed the doors behind them and Luis came forward to take Malcolm's chair and propel it towards the others. He did not look at Rachel and she followed him slowly, conscious of the Marquesa's disapproving stare. However, the Persian rugs on the floor, glowing with colour, attracted her and she forgot the Marquesa as she wondered whether she dared bend and run her fingers over their soft surfaces. Touch was so much a part of her artistic ability, the actual feeling evoked by examining an article, by feeling its texture, was something that could not be simulated.

For a brief period she had forgotten where she was and she was suddenly brought back to the present by Luis's impatient, 'Senhora! I wish to present you to my fiancée, Senhorita Alejento.'

Rachel moved jerkily towards them, conscious of Malcolm's displeasure, realising that he had already been introduced and that she had done the unforgivable thing of forgetting her place.

Amalia's hand was limp and unenthusiastic. She smiled faintly at the English girl and made some polite comment, but afterwards Rachel, for the life of her, couldn't remember what had been said. All she could remember was the feeling of hostility which emanated from all of them, including Malcolm.

Tea was served by another maidservant whom the Marquesa addressed as Juana. She was of a similar age and appearance as Rosa but without her composure. She was nervous as she served the tea, and when Rachel smiled encouragingly at her she received a look of gratitude which was quickly dispersed by the Marquesa's biting tongue. Rachel thought with irony that servants in England would not submit to such tyranny.

She sat in another of the high-backed chairs and tried to listen to the conversation. But it was boring. It began very formally with the Marquesa explaining to Amalia about Malcolm's illness, and subsequent need for recuperation. Amalia was like a sponge, Rachel decided rather uncharitably. But she couldn't help it. The Portuguese girl lapped up words like a cat lapping up cream, but very little emerged in return. Obviously all her life she had been subdued. She could not be very old, about twenty-one, and she was not yet married and therefore not expected to have much conversation in the presence of her elders, but surely she must have some personality.

And what about Luis? thought Rachel reluctantly, biting into a dainty cucumber sandwich. What did she say to him when they were alone together? Or were they ever alone? Was the duenna system still operating here? Surely a man as sophisticated and enlightened as Luis Martinez required more in a wife than beauty and good breeding!

Or did he? After all, his possible main concern was the assurance of the Martinez line, and no doubt Amalia would produce eminently suitable sons to carry on the family name. Rachel felt ashamedly feline at this thought. If ever women were treated as intellectual inferiors it must be here! Unless, perhaps, you happened to be like the Marquesa de Mendao, who now that her husband was dead had assumed all his arrogance. And maybe that was partially due to her English upbringing.

Rachel drank her tea and felt that unsettled feeling stealing over her again. In spite of his attitudes, which she could not agree with, Luis Martinez was an intelligent and virile man. Could he really be satisfied with a wife like Amalia? Would she really be able to hold his interest after the initial period of readjustment was over? Or didn't she care about that? Perhaps it was not uncommon for a man to have other—interests; a mistress, perhaps. Certainly, it seemed unlikely that Luis Martinez would be prepared to spend his intellectual abilities talking with a woman whose whole conversation centred round the family, and as to his physical needs . . .

Rachel shied away from such intimacies. It was nothing to do with her. None of this had anything to do with her, and she was being incredibly foolish even wondering about the lives of these people which were so far removed from her own.

Unwillingly, her eyes drifted to Luis Martinez. She had avoided looking at him up until now, but at the moment he was talking to Amalia and it seemed safe to venture a speculative glance.

In a dark blue suit made, she imagined, of silk, he looked lean and attractive, wholly confident and sure of himself. She thought again of that morning, of his totally unexpected invitation to her, and felt a panicky sense of confinement. She didn't want to stay here, but what could she do? Malcolm seemed determined to exact every ounce of hospitality from the Marquesa, although she herself might as yet be unaware of it.

Rachel bent and lifted her cup, sipping her tea thoughtfully. The china was very thin, almost fragile, transparent when held to the light. Like everything else at the *quinta* it was unique, irreplaceable. She suspected that Malcolm was aware of this, that he intended to leave here with more than just an improvement in his health, and it nauseated her.

She suddenly realised that she was still staring at Luis, and that he had become aware of that scrutiny and was returning it in full measure. Faint colour entered her cheeks at that dispassionate appraisal, and she leant forward to replace her cup on its saucer, the long silky lashes veiling her eyes. But he had made her nervous, her hand shook and misjudged the whereabouts of the saucer, so that the cup fell to shatter into hundreds of tiny pieces on the polished wood floor.

Rachel sprang to her feet, both hands pressed to her mouth in horror, while the shocked silence was broken by the Marquesa's cold angry voice. She, too, had risen, and she stared at Rachel with unconcealed dislike.

'Careless, *careless* girl!' she snapped, her small hands clenched in fury. 'How could you be so stupid?'

Rachel was trembling. The enormity of what she had done was not lost on her and she did not need the Marquesa to tell her what a fool she had been. 'I'm sorry,' she began helplessly, knowing how inadequate were the words. 'I'm sorry.'

'Sorry? Sorry? What use is there in being sorry? Can you tell me that words can replace something so irreplacable?'

'Of course not.' Rachel looked wordlessly towards Malcolm, praying for his support, but he looked furious too. She shook her head. 'I don't know what else I can say.'

'Have you any idea of the value of that small item?' exclaimed the Marquesa. 'Do you realise you have ruined a whole service——'

'That will do, Mama.' Luis's quiet but compelling tones interrupted his mother in full cry. 'I am quite sure that Senhora Trevellyan did not drop the cup on purpose. On the contrary, as she is an artist herself, I doubt her ability to destroy anything so beautiful.'

Rachel was astounded, as no doubt, too, was the Marquesa. That aristocratic little woman drew herself up to her full height and faced her son with almost royal hauteur.

'You would argue with me, Luis?'

Luis had risen to his feet when his mother did, and now he folded his arms and shook his head.

'Senhora Trevellyan is our guest, *amada*. It was an unfortunate accident, nothing more.'

The Marquesa's hands betrayed her agitation. They plucked restlessly at the pearls about her throat. 'It is more than that, Luis. This girl—Senhora Trevellyan then—she is not our guest. She is an interloper here, an *intruder*!'

'*Mae!*' Luis's voice had perceptibly hardened.

'Well, it is true.' The Marquesa's lips moved nervously. 'I did not invite her.'

Rachel felt terrible. It had been bad enough before, but this was worse, much worse. 'I—I——' she tried to begin, only to be silenced by the look on Luis's face.

'I think the distress of losing something that was dear to her heart has momentarily destroyed my mother's sensibilities,' he said forcefully. 'I must ask you to forget what has been said. The matter is closed. We will say no more about it.'

There was a full minute's silence at the end of this announcement, and Rachel looked appealingly towards Malcolm. Now was the moment for him to say something, to make some comment on what had occurred, if only to agree with what Luis had said. But he said nothing. His face was expressionless except when he looked at Rachel and she glimpsed the anger in the depths of his eyes. But whether that anger was directed towards her or towards others in the room she could not be absolutely certain.

Then Amalia spoke. 'Tell me, *senhora*,' she said, addressing herself to Rachel, 'how long do you expect to stay in Portugal?'

Rachel sank down into her chair again with reluctance. The charade was to go on, then. The Marquesa had resumed her seat, and it seemed it was the expected thing to do. What strange, unnatural people these were who could speak so vehemently one minute and then assume a mask of indifference the next.

Swallowing with difficulty, she said: 'I—I'm not sure,' and as she answered the question she wondered whether Amalia was as innocent as she seemed. Was she, in her own subtle way, showing that she too could play her part in the proceedings if she chose?

Malcolm's cup rattled ominously as it was replaced in its saucer on the low table beside him. 'Joanna—the Marquesa, that is—didn't stipulate any specific period for our holiday,' he replied calmly. 'We're old friends. We have a lot of time to make up.'

Amalia's lips thinned. 'Of course, *senhor*. I am aware of your—association with the Marquesa. However, with our wedding...' she glanced significantly at Luis ... 'with our wedding being only a few weeks away, naturally there is a lot to be done——'

'I shall look forward to that.'

Malcolm's succinct interjection was received with varying degrees of surprise and consternation, not least of these from Rachel herself. So he had said it. What now?

'You expect to be here for the wedding...' Amalia's voice trailed away, and Sara Ribialto, who had taken the Marquesa's arm earlier and drawn her back down into her chair, now pressed warning fingers on her employer's wrist.

Luis, as usual, maintained an air of enigmatism. Rachel had no idea what he was thinking as he said: 'We shall see, shall we not, *senhor*. What is it you English say—something about not counting bridges before they are crossed, hmm?' He leant forward and lifted a case of cheroots and offered them to the other man. 'Try these,' he suggested, almost as if the unpleasantness of the last few minutes had never happened. 'I can recommend them.'

Luis's attitude served as an emollient, and because he was choosing to ignore the implications of what had just been said, Malcolm had to do likewise. He accepted a cheroot and allowed Luis to light it for him while Rachel sat there feeling absolutely shattered.

Conversation dwindled inevitably. Not even Luis could sustain any kind of discussion with his mother sitting there with tightly pressed lips and Amalia clearly viewing the whole affair with disapproval. Rachel prayed for Malcolm to say they could go, anything to escape from this awful situation.

Eventually it was the Marquesa who broke up the tea party. She rose to her feet again and pressing a lace handkerchief to her forehead, she said: 'I have a headache, Luis. I'm afraid I must ask you all to excuse me.'

'That's all right, Joanna. We quite understand,' said Malcolm reassuringly, but Rachel sensed that his reassurance did nothing for the Marquesa. She crossed the room to the door slowly, an expression of strain marring her normally composed features, and after she had gone Rachel heaved a heavy sigh.

'I think I should like to go back to our suite now, Rachel,' said her husband then. 'I shall rest before dinner.'

Luis pressed out the remains of his cheroot. He cast a glance in Amalia's direction, and then he said: 'I should like to have a few words with you, Senhor Trevellyan, if I may. In private.'

Rachel, who had got to her feet when her husband spoke, now froze beside her chair. But Malcolm wasn't prepared to be diverted from his own plans.

'Some other time, *senhor*,' he said calmly. 'I am— rather tired.'

Luis's jaw was taut, but there was nothing he could say short of demanding an audience, and it was against his nature to be impolite even to someone who had clearly disturbed his mother. He allowed his gaze to move from the man in the wheelchair to the girl who stood so slim and straight beside her chair, and then he turned away.

'Very well, *senhor*,' he conceded abruptly, and with a rather satisfied little smile Malcolm indicated that Rachel should come and take charge of the wheelchair.

She did so willingly, although she was overwhelmingly conscious of Luis's displeasure and of the fact that Malcolm's relationship with the Marquesa had undertones she had not even suspected.

Back in their suite, she confronted Malcolm tremulously. 'What was all that about?' she demanded.

'What are you talking about, Rachel?' Malcolm assumed a bored expression. 'I should have thought that it was I who should be asking you that question. You were careless, weren't you?'

Rachel rubbed her elbows with her palms. 'It was an accident, you know that.'

'Oh, yes, I know it. But does the Marquesa?'

'What do you mean?'

He shrugged. 'Nothing.' He changed the subject. 'I think I'll sit on the patio for a while. The shadows out there look so cool and appealing.'

Rachel stared at him impotently. 'What's going on, Malcolm? Why are we here?'

'You know why we're here, Rachel. So that I can recuperate.'

Rachel wrung her hands. 'There's more to it than that, I know. Why won't you tell me?'

'I'd like to sit on the patio,' remarked Malcolm mildly, but she could tell he was becoming annoyed.

Sighing, she took the handles of the chair and propelled it outside. In the shade of the balcony she halted and looked upward. The sky was an arc of blue overhead. The shadows were lengthening, and in a short time the deepening colours of evening would darken the courtyard. Their first day in Portugal was drawing to a close, and what a day it had been...

Although Rachel half expected that Luis might come to their suite after dinner to speak to Malcolm, she was mistaken. They dined alone and no one came to disturb them. Afterwards, Malcolm was tired and retired to his bed. It had been an unusually strenuous day for him and Rachel was allowed to seek the refuge of her own rooms. Later, when she checked to see that he was all right, she found him fast asleep, and a spasm of desperation crossed her face. He was completely without conscience, she realised that now, whereas she was filled with anxiety and felt sure she would not close her eyes all night.

In fact, she did fall into a fitful slumber, soon after midnight, but when she awakened next morning she felt dull and listless, and not at all exhilarated as she had done the day before. Too many thoughts tormented her brain, and she made her way along to Malcolm's suite with some misgivings.

They breakfasted indoors again, and then Rosa came to tell them that the Senhora Marquesa had placed a car at their disposal and should they wish to use it they had only to tell her.

Malcolm was in another of his black moods, Rachel had found, and although the knowledge that a car had been provided for them momentarily lifted his spirits, the further information that both the Marquesa and her son were out for the day, visiting with the Alejentos, was sufficient to dampen them again, and he dismissed Rosa without a word of thanks.

Rachel finished her coffee, and then she said: 'Shall we go out for a drive this morning?' in an effort to shift the weight of her own thoughts.

'I don't care to go driving,' muttered Malcolm, pushing aside his plate.

Rachel rested her palms on the cool surface of the silver tray. 'Why not? It's another beautiful morning. Oh, let's get out of here for a while, Malcolm, please!'

He regarded her dourly. 'I've told you. I don't wish to go out.'

'But what am I supposed to do? How can I just wait here for you to decide to do something?'

He drew his brows together. 'Why shouldn't you? You're my wife. I need your company.'

'But you don't. We hardly ever talk together——'

'There's not a lot to say.'

'Then there should be. Malcolm, please, let's go home. At least there I have my—my work.'

He smiled, but it was not a pleasant smile. 'And here you haven't. That's good. That's very good.'

'But why? Surely I'm entitled to have some interests——'

'I don't want to talk any more about it.'

Malcolm rested back against the pillows and closed his eyes. Rachel opened her mouth to say something more and then closed it again. It was useless anyway. Once Malcolm had made up his mind there was nothing she could do to gainsay him. She might just as well accept the situation as continually frustrate herself by trying to change it.

She spent the morning on the patio, wondering whether it would be possible for her to go down to the village that afternoon while Malcolm slept. She had seen a store there. Surely they might sell a phrase book for tourists, and maybe she could buy herself a pad and some crayons. Anything to fill the hours which in these circumstances could only drag.

Malcolm ate an enormous lunch and afterwards was quite willing to relax on his bed. Naturally he expected Rachel to do the same in the heat of the day, and therefore he made no demur about her leaving him alone.

Taking her dark glasses, and her purse, she left the house surreptitiously, hurrying across the courtyard and into the shade of the trees before anyone could see her. It was comparatively easy. The servants all observed the *siesta* and as both the Marquês and the Marquesa were absent there was no one to stop her.

The drive was longer than she remembered, but it was quite pleasant walking in the shade of the trees. The sun was only filtered down to her, and there was a coolness from the shadows.

But once she emerged from the drive, through the gate marked *Privado*, there was a distinct difference. Now the sun beat down upon her head unrelentingly, and the road ahead of her shimmered in a heat haze. It was a dusty track, but luckily no cars were using it at this time of day and she could walk in the road without fear of being choked by dust.

At last the village came into sight, the colour-washed cottages looking cool and inviting. She thought she would go into the café before returning to the *quinta* and have a long cool lemonade, and maybe by then the sun would have lost a little of its violence.

But the worst was yet to come. The shops, the café, everywhere was closed and shuttered against the heat of the day, and she chided herself for her own stupidity. She should have realised that everyone observed the *siesta* here.

She could have cried, so hot and tired did she feel. There was no one about except a couple of old men dozing in the shade of a balcony, while a few dogs roamed aimlessly about. No one to whom she could appeal, no one to give her a few minutes' rest and relaxation.

She looked at the stream, shaded by trees, and thought of paddling there. But she was no peasant girl, and the Marquês would not be pleased to learn a guest in his house had behaved liked one. There was nothing for it but to return to the *quinta*. It might be hours before the shops opened again, and if Malcolm awakened and found she had gone...

The dusty track seemed harder than before. Her sleeveless sweater and jeans left her arms bare and her legs hot and sticky. She felt near to tears when a sleek limousine passed her throwing up a cloud of dust, before halting some few yards ahead of her. Her heart leapt into her throat. What now? Was she to be accosted on top of everything else?

She glanced back towards the village, resisting the impulse to run for safety. She mentally estimated how long it would take her to reach the first of the cottages and then gasped in dismay when a hand caught her arm and swung her round. She raised her other hand to strike her assailant, and then allowed it to fall when she encountered Luis Martinez's dark gaze.

'What are you doing?' he demanded, his face darkened with anger. 'Don't you realise that the sun is dangerous at this hour?'

Rachel shook herself free of him. 'I'm perfectly all

right, thank you, *senhor*,' she retorted with assumed composure.

'But what are you doing out here? What brings you on to this lonely road at the hour of the *siesta*? You should be resting!'

Rachel sighed. 'I—I needed some things, so I went to the stores. I forgot that they observed the *siesta*, too.'

Luis shook his head exasperatedly. 'And you walked all the way from the *quinta*? Why didn't you ask for the car? Then you would have been saved the journey.'

Rachel made a helpless gesture. She had not thought about the car, but even if she had she doubted whether she would have had the temerity to ask for it. Besides, Malcolm might have found out.

'I didn't think of it,' she answered now. After all, that was true.

'Come, then, get in the car. I will take you back to the *quinta* myself.'

Rachel hung back. She had no desire to get into the car with the Marquesa eyeing her with that extreme disapproval she seemed to reserve for her.

Luis frowned. He had started to the car, but she had not moved and now he turned. 'What is wrong? Come!'

'I—I'd rather not.' Rachel coloured. 'Your mother——'

'My mother is not with me!' stated Luis grimly.

'She's not? Oh, but I understand—that is—Rosa told us you were both out for the day——'

'Visiting with the Alejentos? That is right, we were. But my mother is not at all well and she has decided to remain at Alcorado for a few days' rest.'

'I—I see.' Rachel digested this slowly, wondering how Malcolm would react when he learned that his hostess had deserted him.

'So. You will get in the car?' Luis stood regarding her impatiently, disturbingly attractive in his cream silk lounge suit.

'All right.'

Rachel moved forward and when he swung open the passenger side door, she slid in obediently, and he closed it securely behind her. Then he walked round the bonnet and climbed in beside her, turning the ignition without a word.

The car glided forward smoothly, and Rachel felt suddenly weak. It was such a relief to know that she did not have the long drive to negotiate, and she rested her head back against the soft upholstery and half closed her eyes.

But she opened them again a few moments later when they swept past the gate marked *Privado* and continued on down the country road. Looking towards him, she sat upright in her seat and said: 'Where are you taking me?'

He moved his shoulders negligently. 'You'll see. Relax—I am not abducting you. At least, only for a very short period.'

Rachel could not relax, however. She had no idea where he intended taking her, and she dreaded that he might be going to question her about Malcolm's motives for coming to Portugal.

Presently he turned off the road on to a track that wound among some trees while descending towards the river quite steeply. On a ridge above the river he brought the car to a halt and thrusting open his door, slid out.

Rachel remained where she was. Pretty though the spot was she could think of no good reason why he should have brought her here. It had to have to do with Malcolm, and she felt troubled and uneasy.

Luis had stretched and taken off his jacket to drop it

carelessly on to his seat. Then he bent and looked at her, still sitting there.

'Come along,' he said. 'I have something to show you.'

Rachel moved her head slowly from side to side. 'I'd rather go back to the *quinta*,' she said, with what she hoped were firm tones.

Luis's mouth drew in. 'Why? What are you afraid of?'

'Afraid?' Rachel flushed. 'I'm not afraid of anything.'

'Then come with me.' Luis's eyes were challenging.

A disturbing feeling of awareness ran through her. She wanted to go with him, and this time she succumbed. Pushing open her door, she got out, and he gave a slight smile.

'This way,' he said, and walked to the edge of the ridge and vaulted over on to some rocks below.

Rachel hesitated, and with a shrug he went on, leaving her to fend for herself. She scrambled over the ridge, and descended to the rocks below rather less elegantly than he had done, and then followed him, picking her way across the smooth stones.

There were trees at the water's edge, wonderfully cool umbrellas of shade, and she sought the shadows welcomingly. Luis was standing looking down into a rocky basin of water, just below them, a shallow pool, separated from the flowing movement of the river by the rocks.

'There,' he said. 'Do you like it?'

The river flowing tumblingly over the stones, the shadowed arbor beneath the trees, the lush smell of the grassy banks behind them; how could she do otherwise?

'It's lovely,' she said inadequately.

Luis sought a smooth rock and sat down, and she

93

did likewise, her sandalled feet dangling over the pool.

'Don't you want to—paddle?' he queried, rather mockingly, and she realised why he had brought her here. He remembered what she had said on the journey to Mendao two days ago.

Two days! Was that all it was? It seemed like a lifetime!

With a smile she kicked off her sandals and dropped down into the ice-cold water. It was glorious. She rolled up the legs of her jeans to her knees and allowed the water to flow over her ankles. It was so refreshing, so cooling, and she bent to trail her wrists in the water, too.

Then she became conscious of him watching her again, and straightened, drying her hands over the seat of her jeans. She felt infinitely cooler already, but also rather childish.

She climbed out of the water and resumed her seat on the rocks. Luis lit one of his cheroots, and she thought how peaceful it was. There was only the rippling sound of running water and the lazy whistling of the birds to disturb the stillness.

'Thank you,' she said awkwardly. 'I enjoyed that. I feel much cooler now.'

'Good. I'm glad.' He inclined his head.

Rachel looked along at him. He was wearing a white shirt, his tie still knotted to his throat, and on impulse she said: 'Aren't you hot, too?'

Luis looked down at the glowing tip of his cheroot. 'Do women ask such personal questions in your country?'

Rachel bent her head. 'I'm sorry.'

'Why are you sorry?'

'Obviously I shouldn't have asked that question.'

'Did I say so?'

'No, but...' She broke off.

94

'In Portugal we are more formal, I realise this. We observe certain formalities which may seem unnecessary to you. It is the way of things, that is all.'

'But don't you ever want to relax?' she exclaimed, looking at him.

'I am relaxed now,' he returned.

'You can't be.' Rachel made a perplexed gesture. 'In England, on a day as hot as this, a man would take off his shirt, let alone his tie!'

Luis's eyes narrowed. 'You would have me take off my shirt?'

Rachel felt the hot colour burning in her cheeks. It sounded practically indecent the way he said it. 'No,' she said quickly. 'No—that is—I was merely telling you about England.'

'I see.' He considered her broodingly. 'And what else would an Englishman do?'

Rachel drew a trembling breath. 'Why, he—he would sunbathe, I suppose.' She tried to calm the sudden racing of her heart. 'There's no harm in that, is there?'

Luis inhaled deeply on his cheroot. 'And of course, my removing my shirt would not offend you?'

'Offend me? No, of course it wouldn't offend me. Why should it?'

He shrugged, the muscles of his shoulders rippling beneath the thin material of his shirt. 'It is evident that you are not yet aware of the differences between our two countries. I know England. I have spent much time there. I was at university in London. I am conscious of your young people's dislike for convention, and I realise that our ways must seem totally alien to you. But nevertheless, I would venture to state that our ways are the best.'

'How can you say that? What's wrong with people relaxing together?'

'You are deliberately misunderstanding me, I think, *senhora*.' He ground out the stub of his cheroot on the rock beside him. 'A sense of propriety does not preclude social recreation.' His voice had hardened. 'I should have thought with your experience you would have been less willing to support such irresponsibility!'

Rachel was taken aback. 'Irresponsibility?' she echoed. 'What are you talking about?'

Luis sprang to his feet, brushing down his trousers with a careless hand. 'Come, *senhora*!' he said. 'It is time we were getting back to the *quinta*.'

Rachel drew up her knees and pushed her feet into her sandals before standing up. Strands of hair had become loose from the elastic band which secured it and she tugged off the band and refastened it before starting back to the car. Her casual actions were being observed from the ridge, she suddenly realised, where Luis had halted to wait for her, and the realisation brought its own sense of awareness.

She crossed the rocky ledge and began the ascent to the ridge, only to find her sandals had become damp and they slipped on the grassy surface. Inwardly chastising herself, she desperately tried to reach the ridge elegantly, but it was useless, and just when she was about to abandon her sandals and scramble up in a most undignified way, Luis appeared again and bent to offer her his hand.

She placed her hand into his. His hand was cool and hard, as she had imagined, and possessed the kind of latent strength manifest in steel. One strong heave had her securely on the ridge beside him but closer than she had been before. The scent of his body was in her nostrils, a musky, masculine scent that was unexpectedly pleasurable. She, who had never felt any desire for a closer contact with any man, suddenly found herself wondering how it would feel to share with this man the intimacies Malcom forced upon her, whether this man's hard body would arouse her as Malcolm had never been able to do.

Her heart almost stopped beating. She had the wild desire to find out, to move closer to Luis and see whether the touch of her body had any reaction on him.

She looked involuntarily up at him and then drew back abruptly. Luis hesitated only a moment, dark anger burning in the blackness of his eyes, and then he turned and strode back to the car.

Rachel followed slowly. And as she did so she acknowledged that for an instant, for an infinitesimal moment in time, he had become conscious of her as a woman, and would not have repulsed the crazy impulse she had had to touch him. And that was why he had looked so furious—because he had known it, too.

CHAPTER SIX

OVER dinner that evening, Rachel had great difficulty in keeping her knowledge of the Marquesa's where-abouts to herself. It was not her nature to be secretive about anything, but as Malcolm had still been sleep-ing when she returned to the *quinta* that afternoon, she had taken the easiest course and refrained from making any mention of her abortive trip to the village.

It was not until lunch time the following day that Malcolm missed his hostess. He had expected her to visit him, but as the morning passed into afternoon he became suspicious.

'Do you know where Joanna is?' he demanded of Rachel, who was in the process of getting him a drink of water from the jug beside his bed. He had decided to stay in bed earlier, but now he was becoming rest-less.

'How could I?' Rachel moved her shoulders nerv-ously.

Malcolm frowned. 'She was out all day yesterday. The least she could do was to come and see how I am today.'

Rachel handed him the glass of water. 'I doubt whether the Marquesa cares very much one way or the other after your behaviour a couple of days ago,' she commented carefully.

Malcolm caught her wrist as she would have moved away. 'What do you mean by that?'

'You know what I mean. You must know perfectly well that when the Marquesa invited you here she did not expect you to become a permanent fixture.'

Malcolm's grip tightened cruelly and she winced.

'You're hurting me!' she gasped.

'I'll do more than that if I hear any more of that kind of clever talk from you,' he snapped. 'Who the hell do you think you are to talk to me like that?'

Rachel wrenched her wrist out of his grasp, rubbing the reddened flesh painfully. 'I'm only telling you the truth.'

'Are you? Are you? And so what do you think the Marquesa is going to do about it? Throw me out?' His smile was not pleasant. 'Or will she get that arrogant son of hers to do it for her?'

'Malcolm!'

He hunched his shoulders. 'Ring the bell for that girl—what's her name? Rosa? Yes, send for Rosa. She'll know where the old girl is.'

Rachel rang the bell reluctantly. If any of the servants had witnessed her return with Luis the previous afternoon, they must surely expect her to know why the Marquesa was not with them. What if Rosa mentioned that?

But Rosa didn't. Not that she didn't seem surprised at Malcolm's question. She gave them both an encompassing glance, and then replied: 'Did not the Senhor Marquês tell you? The Senhora Marquesa was not well yesterday when she visited with the Alejentos.'

'Not well?' Malcolm leant forward. 'What do you mean?'

'She has been—how do you say it?—overdoing it, *sim*? The wedding, you understand. There is much to arrange.'

'So?' Malcom could scarcely conceal his impatience.

'So the Senhora Marquesa is to spend a few days with her friend Senhora Alejento, *senhor*. You did not know this?'

'No, I didn't know.' Malcolm clenched and unclenched his fists. 'How about her son?'

'The Senhor Marquês is here, *senhor*. You wish to see him?'

Malcolm hesitated. 'Yes. I mean—no, no, not right now. I'll let you know if I want to see him.'

'*Sim, senhor.* Is there anything else?'

Malcolm shook his head and with a faint smile in Rachel's direction Rosa left them.

'So! The old girl's run out on us, has she?' Malcolm breathed deeply. 'Now what does she hope to gain by that, I wonder.'

Rachel tugged at a strand of her hair. 'Does it matter? We're here—taking advantage of her hospitality. I don't see that it matters whether or not the Marquesa is in the *quinta*, too.'

'Well, it matters to me,' snapped Malcolm. 'A hostess doesn't run out on her guests after only a couple of days.'

Rachel sighed. 'Can't we change the subject? When are you going to start using the car?'

Malcolm grimaced. 'I don't know,' he muttered. 'Leave me alone. I want to think.'

After the upheaval of almost a week of activity, it was a relief to have a few days of uninterrupted peace. For the present, it seemed, Malcolm had resigned himself to doing nothing more obstructive than conducting a continual state of conflict with poor Eduardo. He even permitted Rachel to wheel his chair in the grounds, and although these expeditions were something of an ordeal for her, conscious as she was that they might at any time come upon the Marquês himself, they caused Malcolm no such misgivings, and she could not help but admire the magnificently landscaped gardens.

Rosa had offered to do what shopping she might require on her visits to the village, and consequently Rachel seldom, if ever, stirred from their part of the *quinta*. She was restless sometimes, desperate for something to do to fill her time, particularly as Rosa had been unable to find anything in the nature of a phrase book or Portuguese dictionary at the shop.

Malcolm seemed withdrawn most of the time; very rarely did he behave disagreeably towards Rachel, although she was experienced enough to know that this state of affairs would not last. The crisis came when Rachel was summoned to the library one morning.

Rosa brought the message as they were taking coffee. It was about ten days since their arrival at the *quinta*, and the Marquesa's few days with the Alejentos had stretched to a week. Rachel presumed it was about this that the Marquês wanted to see her, but Malcolm was furious.

'What the hell does he mean, sending for you?' he snarled. 'I'm the man of the family; I should be told what's going on, not you.'

'He probably thinks you're still resting,' remarked Rachel placatingly. 'Good heavens, I shan't be very long.'

'But why should he want to see you? He hardly knows you. You've never even had a conversation with him, unless you can call that chat you had in the car coming here from the airport a conversation!' His eyes narrowed. 'Or have you been seeing him behind my back?'

Rachel felt a guilty sense of shame. Was she really as deceitful as she felt? Were her reasons for not telling Malcolm about her two encounters with the Marquês as innocent as she would like to think they were? Shouldn't she have told him anyway and allowed the storm of his anger to pass over her and be done with?

'Malcolm——' she began awkwardly, but he interrupted her.

'I don't want to hear any excuses. No matter what

you say, you must have been encouraging him some-how. How do I know what goes on after you've settled me down for the night? How convenient that you sleep in another room!'

'Malcolm!' Rachel was horrified.

'Well, it's obvious. The man's interested in you. Why else would he send for you and not me? But I won't stand for his bloody insolence!'

'Malcolm, please!' Rachel spread her hands help-lessly. 'You know perfectly well that what you're say-ing is nonsense! The Marquês de Mendao isn't inter-ested in me. How could he be?'

Malcolm's brows drew together. 'How could he be?' he repeated. 'Why shouldn't he be?'

'Oh, Malcolm!' Rachel was exasperated. 'Men like him don't become interested in women like me! You said that yourself.'

'Because you're married?' Malcolm snorted. 'Let me tell you——'

'No! Not because I'm married.' Rachel pressed her palms against each other. 'Simply because I don't move in the same sphere as Luis Martinez!'

Malcolm glared at her. 'You're every bit as good as that prim stuck-up creature he's planning to marry——'

'Goodness doesn't come into it, Malcolm. Look, this is ridiculous! A moment ago you were angry because you thought Martinez might be interested in me. Now you're angry because I tell you he's not—he couldn't be!'

'It's the implication I don't like.' Malcolm hunched his shoulders. 'I've a good mind not to let you go.'

'Oh, Malcolm,' said Rachel again, 'don't be silly. I've got no choice. Or would you rather go in my stead?'

'Huh!' Malcolm chewed at his lower lip. 'Go, then. But don't you dare be longer than ten minutes!'

Rachel heaved a sigh and with a shake of her head left the room.

As the Marquesa had first greeted her in the library, Rachel knew where that room was, although its associations were not of the best. She heard Luis call: *'Entre!'* in reply to her light tap on the panels, and then pushed open the door and entered the room.

Luis was seated at a desk in one corner of the room, but he rose at her entrance and indicated that she should be seated. She sank down into a fan-backed chair upholstered in maroon velvet and waited as he left his desk to cross the Persian carpet towards her. Today he was wearing a honey-coloured denim suit and matching shirt, the narrow trousers accentuating the muscular length of his legs.

'Bom dia, senhora,' he greeted her, and she responded automatically before he went on: 'And how are you today?'

'I'm quite well, thank you, *senhor*,' Rachel was formal. 'I understand you wanted to see me.'

'That is correct, yes.' Luis bowed his head, the thick dark hair smooth and attractive. He had halted some distance from her and was regarding her with that disturbing intensity he could adopt at times, and Rachel moved nervously beneath his stare. She was supremely conscious of the inadequacies of a pair of black velvet pants and a rather crumpled white smock. She wished he would hurry up and say what he had to say and let her go. Apart from the anticipation of Malcolm's anger if she was later than he had signified, she had no des're to prolong the agony of feeling inferior.

But Luis seemed in no hurry to get to his point. He indicated the wine cabinet in the corner, and said: 'You will drink a glass of wine with me, *senhora*?'

'No, thank you, *senhor*.' Rachel looked down at her hands. 'Why did you want to see me?'

Luis thrust his hands into the pockets of his jacket. 'Rosa tells me that you have been endeavouring to obtain a Portuguese phrase book, is this correct?'

Rachel couldn't hide her surprise. 'Why yes, that's right—er—*senhor*.'

He nodded. 'I see. And you did not consider asking me whether there might not be such a book in the *quinta*?'

Rachel shook her head. 'I—it seemed an impertinence. Besides, I thought I'd be able to buy one quite easily.'

'Rosa further tells me that you purchased some paper and crayons.'

Rosa had obviously reported all her purchases to the Marquês. Rachel felt rather annoyed. How dared he pry into her affairs like this?

'Yes, that's right,' she agreed. 'I also bought some face tissues, a comb, some razor blades for Malcolm, and a pair of tights!'

Luis's mouth had drawn into a tight line. 'You are insolent, *senhora*!' he said coldly.

Rachel was unrepentant. 'Am I? And don't you think it's rather insolent for you to question Rosa about my private purchases?'

He caught his breath angrily. 'Have a care, *senhora*. I do not permit anyone to speak to me like that!'

'Oh, don't you?' Rachel had risen to her feet now and faced him furiously. 'Then you shouldn't behave as though you have a certain *droit du seigneur* to know every small thing I do!'

He took a step towards her, his face a mask of anger, and she stepped back a pace, half afraid of the look in his eyes.

'I did not question Rosa about your purchases,' he snapped, his fists clenched into balls within the confines of his pockets, almost as though he did not trust himself to bring them out. 'She came to me and told me that she thought you were bored, *senhora*. She said she had tried to get you a phrase book but that the village stores did not sell such a thing. She said you had even bought some crayons and a drawing tablet. She was concerned for you. I think she was afraid you were desperate enough to seek the diversions of a child. She did not understand, until I explained, that you might use the crayons and tablet for sketching.'

Rachel listened to his explanation with a growing sense of humiliation. When he had finished she spread her hands in a deprecatory way. 'I'm sorry,' she murmured awkwardly. 'Oh, heavens, I always seem to be saying that to you.'

The Marquês's fists relaxed. He took his hands out of his pockets and folded them behind his back. The movement opened the jacket of his denim suit, revealing the width of his chest beneath. One of the buttons of his shirt had become unfastened, and pulled apart, as now, she could see the darkness of hair on his chest.

Startled at the strange emotions the sight of his body aroused within her, she looked quickly up at him and encountered his eyes. But then she was unable to sustain his stare and her eyes dropped down to that carelessly opened button again and from thence down the length of his body to his suede-booted feet.

Now it was Luis who seemed disturbed by her appraisal. He turned abruptly away, and walked back to his desk.

'I accept your apology,' he said stiffly, 'and now I suggest we come to the point of this meeting.'

'Yes, *senhor*.' Rachel resumed her seat again, mostly because her legs had become ridiculously weak suddenly.

He came back to her carrying two books. 'Many years ago, when my mother first came to Mendao, she too had to learn our language. These were her grammar textbooks. I thought they might be of some use to you.'

Rachel took the books jerkily and turned them over in her hands, nervously glancing at the titles. 'That—that was very kind of you, *senhor*,' she murmured.

Luis watched her as she examined them and then turned away again. He walked to the exquisitely tiled fireplace and raised a foot to rest it on the polished brass fender. Then he looked back at her. 'Tell me,' he said quietly, 'do you find your life here at the *quinta* so boring?'

Rachel didn't know how to answer him. She moved her shoulders in a helpless gesture. 'I wish I could work,' she confessed unhappily.

'You mean—paint?'

'That's right.' Rachel smoothed her fingers over the fine leather of one of the volumes. 'I—when Malcolm is resting, I find—time drags.'

'I see.' Luis opened a carved box on the mantelshelf and extracted a cheroot. Placing it between his teeth he lit it with a small gold lighter from his pocket. Then he inhaled deeply before saying: 'If it is of any small interest to you, this library possesses many books about artists and their work. In addition to which there are some extremely fine examples of art and sculpture about the *quinta*. Myself, I prefer Dégas, and other painters of the Impressionist school, but our collection in no way wholly reflects my tastes. Perhaps when—when your husband is resting, you would care to familiarise yourself with the collection.'

Rachel pressed the books tightly to her breast. 'That's very kind of you, *senhor*. But ...' She paused. But—what? But she knew without asking what Malcolm's reaction to Luis's suggestion would be. 'But I—I——'

His expression hardened as it was wont to do whenever her feelings came into conflict with his. 'You are about to refuse, *senhora*? Why? Is my offer so distasteful to you?'

'It's not distasteful at all,' exclaimed Rachel miserably. 'On the contrary, I would love to examine these books—the paintings; I adore sculpture! But it's not as simple as that. My—my husband likes to know I'm around, even when he's resting. I don't think he would —approve of me wandering round the building.'

Luis frowned. His dark eyes bored into hers. 'Let me understand this, *senhora*,' he said grimly. 'You say your husband would object to you spending an hour of each day doing that which you enjoy?'

Rachel felt awful. Put that way, it sounded terrible. 'He's not a well man, *senhor*.'

'Is he not?' His tone was dry. 'It would seem to me that your husband is a selfish man, *senhora*.' He took his foot from the fender and stood straight. 'Either that, or you are deceiving me.'

Rachel got to her feet. 'I think I should be going, *senhor*,' she said. 'I—I've wasted enough of your time. Thank you for the books——'

'A moment.' He came across the floor towards her, halting only a couple of feet from her. 'What is it you are afraid of? Your husband? Or me?'

Rachel's anxious eyes betrayed her agitation. 'Afraid, *senhor*?' she echoed. 'Why should I be afraid —of anyone?'

'Indeed.' He continued to look at her, and her gaze again dropped before his. She concentrated on the buckle at the waist of his trousers, and prayed that he would not prolong this interview. 'Would you like me to speak to your husband on your behalf?'

Rachel blinked rapidly, looking upward. 'Oh, no,

no, don't do that! I—I'll see what he says. It's just his way——'

'I can see he is a possessive man also,' went on Luis quietly. 'Eduardo tells me it is very rarely that he permits him to assist him. You do everything for him.'

'Yes, *senhor*.'

'I do not like this in my house!' said Luis vehemently. 'A woman should not be expected to perform manual tasks!'

'I don't mind, really.' Rachel took a step backward. 'I really should be going . . .'

He ran his hand down his shirt front in a gesture of impatience and encountered the unfastened button. Immediately he fastened it, and Rachel's eyes were drawn to the lean beauty of his hands. She thought of Amalia Alejento, and of how, soon, she would respond to the mastery of his lovemaking, and feel those hard, brown hands against her magnolia-white skin . . .

The pictures that these thoughts evoked were suddenly unbearable to her. She turned carelessly, and stumbled over her chair, the books flying wildly from her hands as she fell clumsily on to the polished floor.

Immediately, the thing that she had imagined came about. With an exclamation of concern, Luis came down on his haunches beside her and gripping her shoulders helped her to her feet.

'*Meu Deus!*' he exclaimed. 'Are you all right?'

Rachel nodded. His fingers were still on her shoulders, his thumbs sliding off the neckline of the smock to smooth the bones of her throat. A throbbing awareness of the dangerousness of this situation was invading every bone in her body, and she had to drag herself away from him to stand trembling before him.

'I—I'm all right,' she stammered, looking round for the books. 'I'm sorry I was so careless.'

She made to bend down for the scattered books, but

he forestalled her, lifting them himself and folding the pages into place again. Then he held them out to her and she took them, but as she did so, he gripped her wrist.

'You are so thin!' he muttered huskily. 'Is the food at the *quinta* not to your liking?'

Rachel felt choked. 'The food's—very nice,' she managed. 'Please! I must go.'

'*Por amor de Deus!*' he muttered, between his teeth. 'Why did you have to marry Trevellyan? Other women have managed alone. Why couldn't you?'

Rachel was horrified. She tore her wrist out of his grasp and made for the door, and he let her. She felt certain he was furious with himself for allowing any concern for her to show.

She let herself out into the hall, closing the door and standing there trembling for several minutes before she could summon up enough energy to make her way back to the suite—and Malcolm.

And it was not until much later that she remembered exactly what he had said, and wondered what he had meant by it.

CHAPTER SEVEN

To her surprise, Malcolm took Luis's gift of the books quite calmly, more calmly than she would have thought possible after the way he had behaved earlier. But something had happened to put him in an extremely good mood, and although she had no idea what it could be, she didn't question her good fortune.

He asked what the Marquês had wanted her for, and she told him, omitting the part about the library and the collection. There was no point in antagonising him unnecessarily, and besides, even were he to grant his permission, she doubted very much whether she would take advantage of Luis's offer. There were other things to consider, not least of these being the reaction being thrown into constant proximity with Luis might have on her. That way lay danger; this morning had proved that.

All the same, it was a temptation, and the following afternoon, while Malcolm was sleeping, she felt an intense longing to go to the library and probe the pages of some ancient tome. But she didn't! She spent her time instead, sketching the view from her bedroom window.

The days passed by. The Marquesa had still not returned, and Rachel was aware that Malcolm was becoming suspicious of this prolonged visit. His good humour towards Rachel had long since evaporated again, and she was constantly in attendance on him, running to his every command in a sincere desire to avoid conflict.

She had no idea how Luis spent his days. Occasionally, Rosa would enlighten them with the knowledge that the Senhor Marquês had gone to Coimbra on business, or that he was visiting the vineyards in a neighbouring valley, or perhaps dining with his fiancée and her family at Alcorado; but mostly their lives ran along parallel lines, never touching and never crossing. They might have been alone in the *quinta*.

Undoubtedly, Rachel decided, this was the best solution to their situation here. Without the Marquesa's presence they had no point of contact with the other side of the household, and they could conduct their lives as they chose.

But Malcolm did not see it this way. He continually chafed at being 'segregated', as he put it, and began thinking of a way in which he might impose his presence on Luis.

One morning he had Rachel, much against her better judgement, wheel his chair along the corridor and across the hall and into the main *sala*. But it was, for him, a wasted expedition. Only the maid Juana found them there, and she was quick to explain in her broken English that the Senhor Marquês was away for the day buying horses. Rachel was unutterably relieved; she would have hated to have been discovered in such a situation by Luis, but Malcolm was angry and was scarcely civil for the remainder of the day. He went to bed early, and was fast asleep at nine-thirty when there was a tap at the door of their *sala*.

Rachel, who had been sitting reading, went to answer it, and stood back in surprise when she found Luis outside.

'Yes, *senhor*.' Rachel resumed her seat again, mostly into the *sala*.

'I understand your husband wishes to see me, *senhora*.'

'What—what gave you that idea?' She was uneasy.

'The maidservant Juana. She told me that you were

111

in the main *sala* this morning looking for me.'

Did nothing in this house happen without him becoming aware of it?

Rachel put all her weight on one foot and then on the other. 'Well, I'm sorry—but I'm afraid Malcolm is asleep right now.'

Luis's gaze shifted to her face. 'Isn't it rather early for him to be sleeping, *senhora*?'

Rachel stiffened. 'Don't you believe me?'

'Of course I believe you.' He sighed impatiently. 'Do you know why he wanted to see me?'

Rachel felt dreadful. 'Not—not really, no.'

'I see.' Luis paused. Then: 'You use these rooms in preference to your own?'

'No, not at all. I was reading, that's all. I stay here until Malcolm is settled down for the night. As a matter of fact, I was studying those books you lent me and I'm afraid I forgot the time.'

He nodded slowly. 'And now? What now? Do you retire early, too?'

Rachel lifted her slim shoulders. 'Sometimes.'

'Tonight. What about tonight?'

'I don't know.' Rachel glanced nervously towards Malcolm's closed door. He was asleep, it was true, but if the Marquês continued talking in these low, penetrating tones he would soon not be. 'Why do you ask?'

Luis stood stiffly. 'I was about to ask whether you would care to walk for a while in the grounds, *senhora*.'

Rachel tucked her hair behind her ears. It was loose tonight and she was suddenly conscious that it was probably untidy. 'Well—I'm not really dressed to go anywhere, *senhor*.' She was wearing a dress for once, a simple yellow cotton, with a low round neckline and no sleeves. It was short, too, shorter than anything Amalia Alejento would be likely to wear, Rachel felt sure, and her legs were bare. Compared to his lean elegance in the dark brown lounge suit he was wearing she felt like a peasant. 'I—it's very kind of you——'

'Do not say those words to me again!' he snapped shortly. 'It is not kind, not kind at all. I wish your company, that is all.'

Rachel's heart pounded in her ears. 'I don't know what to say.'

'Then say yes. Take pity on me!'

Pity! Rachel could think of no one less desirous of pity. She looked into the dark eyes and felt her resolution deserting her. Tearing her gaze away, she said: 'Malcolm might wake. I should be here.'

'Very well, *senhora.*' He was obviously accepting her refusal. Rachel's palms felt moist. Where was the harm in walking with him? What did she expect him to do to her? Attack her? The Marquês de Mendao was not the kind of man to do any such thing.

He bowed his head and was turning away when she halted him.

'*Senhor!* I will come with you.'

The dark eyes narrowed. 'Very well, *senhora.* Shall we go?'

Rachel hesitated only a moment longer and then with a slight shrug she went out of the door and closed it silently behind her.

It was amazingly cool outside after the heat of the day, but not cool enough for Rachel to need a coat. On the contrary, she enjoyed the faint breeze that fanned her arms and neck. All the scents of the day had been intensified by the coming of night, the perfumes of the flowers lingering long after the last rays of the sun had disappeared below the horizon.

Luis walked with his hands folded behind his back, strolling beside her silently. For the moment it seemed he had nothing to say, and Rachel tried to calm her tautened nerves. She was being ridiculous, feeling this way. Just because a man had asked her to take a walk with him! She was so stupidly inexperienced where men were concerned, her only criterion the careless cruelty of her husband.

At last he said: 'I went to Oporto today. A friend of mine was selling some horses. I bought a rather fine colt. Would you like to see him?'

Rachel made a deprecatory gesture. 'I'd love to.'

'*Bom!* We will go to the stables. It is this way.'

The stables were not far from the house, but the path was shadowy in places and Rachel followed close behind the Marquês. This was an area she had not seen before and she silently admired the white-painted buildings and cobbled forecourt.

Everything was locked up for the night, but Luis took some keys out of his pocket and unfastened the padlock which secured the stable door. Then he went inside and lit some lamps before signifying that Rachel should join him.

There were three horses housed in this building, and they came to their rails nuzzling Luis for sugar and sweetmeats. He spoke to all of them, and Rachel, following, realised he felt a real affection for the beasts.

At the end of the row, a slim, nervous-looking animal whinnied impatiently. It was all black, the muscles of its body rippling smoothly beneath its coat. It was quite magnificent, and Luis gave a rather satisfied smile.

'This is Arrojado,' he said. 'Which means daredevil! Isn't he beautiful?'

'Beautiful,' echoed Rachel, going forward to stroke the colt's muzzle. 'Who chose his name?'

'I did,' replied Luis, bending under the rail and going into the stall with the animal. He ran his hand lightly along the jerking muscles of its back. '*Fique*

114

tranquilo, Arrojado. *Calma!*'

Rachel leant on the rail watching him. Under his gentle reassurance, the colt stopped its heavy breathing and began nuzzling him as the other horses had done. When Luis smiled, as he was smiling at the animal, he looked quite devastatingly attractive, and Rachel wondered if he smiled at Amalia Alejento like that. What did they talk about when they were alone together? Did he kiss her, caress her, make love to her? Her lips trembled and she turned away, forcing herself to move to another stall where she could not see Luis. It was nothing to do with her, so why did she continually think about it? How could she have this disturbing knowledge that a woman like Amalia would never make a man like Luis happy? She had no real idea what did or did not make him happy.

Luis ducked out of Arrojado's stall and strode along the gallery to where Rachel was standing. She didn't look at him but slowly began to walk towards the open door. Her impulse was to hurry, but she didn't want to arouse his curiosity by behaving foolishly.

Outside, the cool night air was a balm to her hot face, and she stood hugging herself while he closed the door again and secured the padlock.

Then he dropped the keys into his pocket again, and said: 'Do you ride, *senhora*?'

Rachel shook her head. 'I'm afraid not.'

'Wouldn't you like to learn?'

'Perhaps.' She was cautious.

'I could teach you.'

Rachel drew a deep breath. 'Shall we be going back now?'

She heard his swiftly disguised imprecation. 'As you wish.'

Rachel turned and followed the path which brought them out through the trees to the side of the drive. It was amazing how surely she found her way, but fear had quickened her step and her awareness. But fear of what? She was being ridiculous again.

They entered the *quinta* through french doors into the *sala*. Only one lamp burned in here, and the large room was shadowy. Rachel saw the exquisite ornamentation she had admired on the afternoon of that disastrous tea party and walked carefully between the small tables, half afraid of damaging some other unique object.

The doors to the hall were closed and as she reached for them, Luis said: 'Won't you stay and have a drink with me before you go to bed?'

Rachel turned, resting back against the carved panels of the doors. 'I don't think that's a very good idea,' she said.

'Why not?' He had closed the french doors and was standing regarding her intently.

Rachel sighed. 'If—if your fiancée were here, Senhorita Alejento, would she be permitted to stay and have a drink with you before going to bed, *senhor*?'

'No.'

'Why not?'

'Amalia is a single woman, what you would call—a maiden; it would not be fitting for her to stay and have a drink alone with me.'

'I see. But it's all right for me.'

He moved towards a tray of drinks resting on a table in a corner. 'Let us not enter into an argument, *senhora*. You are at liberty to refuse my offer.'

'Yes, I am, aren't I? Very well then, I refuse.'

He poured himself some brandy and swallowed half of it at a gulp before turning to face her the glass in his hand. 'I wish you would not,' he said.

Rachel stared at him, her eyes troubled. 'Why?

Why, for heaven's sake? Why do you want my company?'

Luis's expression darkened. Even across the width of that enormous room she saw the anger in their depths. 'Is it not sufficient that I do?' he demanded, crossing to stand only a few yards from her.

'No. No, it's not.' Rachel's mouth was working. 'I don't understand you—oh, *senhor*!' She added his title almost impatiently. 'I—I wish you would leave me alone!'

'Do you?' He swallowed the remainder of his brandy and then studied the empty glass almost without realising he was doing so.

'I'd better go.'

Rachel straightened away from the door, and put her hand behind her back, seeking the handle. But she couldn't find it, and she turned jerkily to do so.

'Allow me, *senhora*.'

He was right behind her, reaching past her to take the handle and pull the door wide. For an instant he was close to her again, as he had been that day by the river. Only this time his arm brushed her body and she had only to turn to press her face against his chest. The urge to do so was overpowering. To touch him, any part of him! She could feel the fine material of his jacket against her arm, and smell his breath with its faint odour of brandy.

'Oh, Luis!' she murmured, almost under her breath, but he heard her. He looked down at her searchingly, almost angrily, she thought, and with a helpless shake of her head, she added: 'I'm sorry, I'm sorry. I shouldn't have said that, *senhor*!'

'So you think of me as Luis,' he murmured huskily, not moving away from her. 'Say it again!'

'What?' Rachel felt as though she couldn't get her breath.

'My name; say it again!'

'Luis.' Rachel spoke convulsively. 'I'm—I'm sorry.'

His breathing had quickened now, she could hear it, she could *feel* it. She could see the tautened muscles of his wrist on the hand that had reached for the door handle. She could feel his eyes moving over her like a lick of flame across her flesh.

'*Deus*, Rachel!' he groaned hoarsely, and the door slammed shut again. '*Tu queria...*'

But when he moved forward to imprison her against the door with the weight of his body, she moved with astonishing speed, jack-knifing out of his reach.

'No!' she exclaimed chokingly. 'No, Luis! I—I'm not that kind of woman!'

He turned. Now he was resting against the door and he ran a hand over the thickness of his hair almost dazedly. 'What are you talking about?' he asked, his voice thickened by his emotions.

Rachel pressed both hands to her breast. 'I want to go now,' she said unsteadily. 'Please—please open the door!'

Luis looked at her for several minutes and then he seemed to come to his senses. With a hardening of his jaw, he straightened and pulling open the door stood to one side stiffly.

Rachel didn't look at him as she walked quickly out of the room.

The following morning Rachel looked tired and strained. She had slept very badly, and when she went along to Malcolm's suite she was totally unprepared for his first words:

'Did you enjoy yourself last night, Rachel?'

She halted in the middle of opening the shutters. Her hands shook, and she stared uncomprehendingly at him. 'What—what did you say?'

Malcolm looked smug. He hoisted himself up on to his pillows and smiled unpleasantly at her. 'I asked whether you enjoyed yourself last night,' he repeated.

'Last—last night——' she faltered.

'Yes, last night. You went out into the grounds, didn't you? After I was safely tucked up in my bed!'

Rachel turned back to the shutters. She felt sick. Malcolm knew that Luis had come here last evening. He must have heard them talking as she had been afraid he might. Deciding to make a clean breast of it, she said: 'I thought you were asleep. I'm sorry if you feel I shouldn't have gone.'

She waited for the storm to break, but it didn't. She turned back to him. 'Did—did you hear what I said, Malcolm?'

'Yes, I heard.' Malcolm's face wore a strange expression.

Rachel frowned. 'And you—don't mind?'

'Why? Is there something I should mind?' Malcolm became suddenly aggressive.

'No!' Rachel took a step away from him. 'No, of course not.'

Her vehemence must have satisfied him because he nodded his head slowly and the anger left his voice. 'No, of course not. You're not like that, are you, Rachel? You're not interested in men! I sometimes wonder what you are interested in!' His lips twisted. 'But he doesn't know that, does he? And it's becoming pretty obvious he's more than a little interested in you!'

'Oh, don't be ridiculous, Malcolm!' Rachel didn't want him to put into words the thing she was becoming most afraid of.

His face changed again. 'I'm not silly! I heard him last night—asking you to take a walk with him. I wonder what his mother would say to that! And that whey-

119

faced Alejento girl. What a shock it would be for her to learn that her so aristocratic fiancé isn't above making passes at a married woman!'

Rachel gasped. 'He—he didn't make passes!' she denied hotly.

'Didn't he?' Malcolm shrugged. 'In their book, even coming here and taking you walking is tantamount to a flirtation——'

'But he didn't come here to take me walking,' she protested. 'He came to see you. He had heard about us being in the *sala* yesterday morning, and he thought you wanted to see him. Heavens, if you were awake, why didn't you let me know? You could have talked to him.'

'It didn't suit my purpose to do so,' retorted Malcolm. 'I was curious to know how far he would go. Poor Joanna! She thought she could escape me by leaving the *quinta*. The idea of her son being anything less than incorruptible never even entered her head.'

'What are you talking about, Malcolm?' Rachel felt that awful uneasy feeling again. 'Why should you want to corrupt the Marquesa or her son?'

Malcolm adopted an innocent attitude. 'Did I say I did?'

'No, but—oh, Malcolm, it's obvious we're not welcome here. Let's go home. Please!'

'No!' Malcolm was adamant. 'I'm not finished here. Not by a long chalk.'

Rachel turned away. What was the use? No matter what happened, Malcolm was determined to exact his pound of flesh, but what that pound of flesh might turn out to be, she had no idea.

She was discussing with Rosa the possibility of her obtaining some material for Rachel so that she could make herself a couple of cheap dresses when the Marquês arrived later that morning. He strode through the open door of the *sala* and said in imperative tones:

'Where is Senhor Trevellyan? I wish to speak with him?'

Rachel twisted her hands together, avoiding his eyes. 'He—he's in the bedroom, *senhor*,' she replied, and got no further before Luis had crossed the room and after a peremptory knock had thrust open the door and entered the bedroom.

Rosa's dark eyes widened in astonishment. '*Ceus!*' she exclaimed, clasping her hands. 'The Senhor Marquês—he is very angry, is he not?'

Rachel swallowed with difficulty. 'Is he?'

'But of course, *senhora*. Did you not see his face? I have never known him do such a thing before.'

'Such a thing as what?'

'To come into a guest's room without first obtaining permission, and then to ask to see your husband without first a greeting! No, *senhora*, the Senhor Marquês is very angry.'

Rachel quivered. Her momentary interest in the dresses had waned. She had thought the activity might give her something to do, might act as a distraction for her thoughts. But it was useless. How could she concentrate on anything, aware as she was of the precariousness of their position here?

Rosa bustled away. Obviously she considered it would not be politic to be still about when the Marquês emerged from Senhor Trevellyan's bedroom. Rachel agreed to talk to her later, and then after the girl had gone she went out on to the patio.

It was very hot, and she stretched her length in one of the low loungers. Her instincts urged her to leave Malcolm's suite and seek the comparative sanctuary of her own suite of rooms, but Malcolm might conceivably call her and she had to remain on hand to avoid arousing any further speculation on his part. What a situation! Her head ached when she thought about it, and determinedly she picked up the tablet and crayons which lay on the glass-topped table nearby and began sketching. Her crayon moved swiftly and surely across the paper and the outline of a man's head began to take shape. Deep-set eyes, high cheekbones, a thin, intelligent profile, a lower lip with a hint of sensuality; she stared at the face taking shape almost irritably. Couldn't she even escape from her thoughts in her work now? She had always been able to do so. It had been the one inviolable part of her existence and that was why Malcolm had resented it. But it seemed even that was to be denied her.

She tore off the sheet and screwed it into a ball and threw it on the mosaic tiling of the patio. She would not look at such a revealing example of her own vulnerability.

She looked behind her, towards the french doors leading into the *sala*. Was Luis still with Malcolm, or had he slipped away without her being aware of it? But no. If he had gone, Malcolm would be sure to send for her. So what was going on? Why had he come this morning? What were they talking about?

She was staring blindly at the blank page in front of her when she heard the door of Malcolm's bedroom open and Luis emerged. She did not look round, but he came out on to the patio and stood stiffly beside her chair.

'*Bom dia, senhora*,' he said, just as stiffly. 'How are you this morning?'

Rachel glanced upward, but only as high as his jacket lapels. 'I'm very well, thank you. And you?'

'Rachel! Rachel, where are you?'

The sound of Malcolm shouting her name echoed loudly round the small courtyard. Rachel sighed and putting aside her sketching tablet made to get to her feet. But Luis's next words made her hesitate.

'I came to apologise,' he said quickly, in a low tone. 'For last night.' His voice was cool. 'I don't know what came over me. I apologise. It won't happen again.'

Rachel got to her feet then, smoothing the sleeves of her blouse, brushing the sides of her trousers. Still not looking at him, she said: 'That's quite all right, *senhor*.'

'Rachel, where the hell are you?'

Malcolm was growing impatient, and Rachel gave an apologetic gesture and made for the french doors. She heard Luis's barely concealed expletive, but then she was entering Malcolm's bedroom and he was indicating that she should close the door behind her.

'What the hell have you been doing?' he snapped angrily. 'I've been calling you for ages!'

'No, you haven't, Malcolm,' she replied carefully. 'I —I was just outside—on the patio. You can't expect me to run every time you call.'

Malcolm hunched his shoulders. 'You saw *him* arrive, I suppose?'

'You mean—the Marquês?'

'Of course I mean the Marquês. Don't play games with me, Rachel!'

'I'm not.' She lifted her shoulders. 'Well? What did he want?'

'He wanted to know how soon we'd be leaving!'

'What?' Rachel could hardly believe her ears. 'And —and what did you tell him?'

'The same as I've told you. I'll go when I'm ready and not before.'

Rachel gasped. 'What did he say?'

'He said I had another week and then he was afraid he would have to ask us to leave!'

Rachel sank down on to the side of the bed. 'I see.'

She moved her head a trifle dazedly. 'Well, that's something anyway.'

'What—is something?'

'Staying another week, of course. Oh, it'll be nice to go home——'

'We're not going home!'

'But you just said——'

'I said that was what *he* had said. I didn't say I agreed with it.'

'But—but you can't stay here against his wishes! He—he could have you—ejected!'

'I doubt whether Joanna will agree to that.'

'The Marquesa's not here.'

'I know. But she will be.'

'What do you mean? Is she coming back to the *quinta* soon?'

Malcolm plucked at the satin bedcovering. 'I think she might.'

Rachel gave a helpless sigh. 'Oh, Malcolm! What on earth is the use of antagonising these people? We've been here two weeks—three, if you count next week as well. Surely that's long enough for you!'

'I shall need some powerful stimulant to encourage me to leave,' remarked Malcolm unpleasantly. 'I didn't come all this way just to spend a few weeks in the sun.'

'Then what did you come for?' Rachel stared at him with tormented eyes.

'You'll learn one day. Now, go and tell Eduardo I want to see him.'

'Eduardo?' Rachel was astonished. 'What do you want to see Eduardo for?' She glanced round. 'If you want to get up, I can help you as I'm here.'

'Don't ask questions. Just get him!'

Malcolm's mouth was hard, and Rachel got obediently to her feet. The whole situation appalled her, and she wished there was some way she could back out of it. She didn't want to stay here. She wanted nothing from the Martinez family, and in spite of Malcolm's aggressive attitude she didn't see how he could force his will on them. Perhaps she was being unnecessarily pessimistic. Perhaps they would leave in a week's time as Luis wanted. Certainly, as far as she was concerned, it was the only solution.

CHAPTER EIGHT

THE following morning Malcolm surprised Rachel by asking her to arrange for the car to be put at their disposal.

'You're going out?' she exclaimed.

'*We* are going out,' corrected Malcolm suavely. 'I thought it was time we saw something of the countryside.'

Rachel hesitated. What did this mean? Was Malcolm about to accept Luis's ultimatum and leave in a week as expected? Oh, she hoped it was true!

The car that was made available to them was a pale blue convertible, with chrome slashes along the sides. It was a beautiful vehicle and ideal for such a climate. Their chauffeur was Eduardo, and Rachel paused to wonder whether that was why Malcolm had wanted to speak to him the day before. She shook her head. Perhaps she was too quick to seek for ulterior motives when it came to dealing with her husband, but past experience had made her unnaturally cautious.

Apart from the day she had walked to the village, it was the first time they had left the *quinta* since their arrival, and in spite of her misgivings, Rachel found herself relaxing as the beautiful building and its incumbent problems disappeared from sight. She sat in the back with Malcolm and tried not to speculate on why he should be looking so pleased with himself.

They drove through the valley, past groves of citrus and olive trees, acres of crops where black-clad peasant women worked, impervious to the heat, it seemed. Rachel wondered how they could bear to wear so many clothes. Even the young women wore scarves over their heads. Occasionally, a hand would be raised in acknowledgement of the car. Obviously all the Marquês's vehicles were instantly recognisable; but when it was seen that the Marquês was not with them they merely received curious stares.

The road wound inland through the hills and presently dropped into another valley. They came upon a village, like Mendao, with a few cottages and a store, and a church surrounded by a graveyard. Rachel would have liked Malcolm to stop, but he shook off her restraining hand and said: 'We don't have time.'

Rachel stared at him. 'Time? I should have thought we had all the time in the world.'

'Well, we haven't. Drive on, Eduardo. Is it much further?'

Eduardo glanced behind him at his passengers. '*Nao, senhor. Mas, nao gosto. Espero que o Senhor Marquês*——'

'What the hell are you muttering about, man?' Malcolm silenced him angrily. 'If you have anything to say, say it in English!'

Rachel frowned, trying to translate what Eduardo had said. *Nao* meant no, she knew, and she thought he had said that he didn't like it. But what? What didn't he like? And why had he mentioned Luis's name in that worried way?

She looked helplessly at her husband, but he ignored her and she looked out at the passing scenery with a rising sense of anxiety. Where were they going? Where had Malcolm instructed Eduardo to take them that was worrying the young Portuguese so much?

They turned off the main road on to a side track, passing through an open gateway before following the drive of a house and presently coming to a halt before double panelled doors which stood wide to the air.

Rachel took one look at Malcolm's smug face and

then looked back at the building. It was a country house, smaller than the Quinta Martinez, and lacking its charm and beauty. Nevertheless, it was quite an attractive building in mellowed stone, tall chimneys rising above a sloping roof.

'Where are we?' she asked uneasily. 'Eduardo! What is this?'

'*Esta* Alcorado, *senhora!*'

'*Alcorado!*' Rachel pressed her hands to her cheeks. 'The—the home of Senhorita Alejento?'

'*Sim, senhora.*'

'Oh!' Rachel was horrified. She turned on Malcolm. 'What are you thinking of? Why have we come here?' She looked desperately at Eduardo. 'Drive on, Eduardo. Don't wait. Take us back to the *quinta* at once!'

'Don't you dare!' Malcolm was so incensed he flung himself forward in his seat and caught Eduardo by the throat. 'Get my chair out of the boot, and be quick about it!'

Eduardo stumbled out of the car and went to get the chair. It was obvious that Malcolm terrified him and Rachel could expect no help from him. But she refused to be a party to this horrible fiasco.

'Have you taken leave of your senses, Malcolm?' she cried. 'Why have you come here? You can't mean to ask to see the Marquesa!'

'Can't I? Why not? If the mountain won't come to Mahomet...'

'Malcolm, can't you see this is crazy! People don't do things like this!'

'Shut up. You know nothing about it. This is between Joanna and me.'

'Then why have you brought me along? Why am I to be dragged into it?'

'What would you have had me do? Leave you at the *quinta* to hold hands with the Marquês? No, thanks!'

Rachel's cheeks burned. 'You can't be serious! Why, only yesterday——'

'*Eduardo!* Where the hell are you, man? Get me out of this car!'

The sound of their raised voices had carried on the still humid air. A black-clad manservant appeared in the doorway at the head of the flight of steps leading up to the entrance, and was looking down on them with unconcealed hostility. But then he seemed to recognise the car, and he came hastening down the steps towards them.

'*Bom dia, senhor, senhora!*' he greeted them politely. '*Posso ajuda-lo?*'

Malcolm nodded. 'Yes, you can tell the Marquesa de Mendao that she has a visitor!'

'*O Marquesa, senhor?*' The man looked concerned. Then he added in English: 'The Marquesa is expecting you, *senhor?*'

Eduardo had brought round Malcolm's folding chair and was helping him into it. He looked up rather nervously at his counterpart and the other man repeated: 'The Marquesa is expecting you, *senhor?*'

Malcolm looked up from his position in the chair. 'No—no, she's not expecting me. It's to be a—surprise.' He smiled, but it did not reach his eyes. 'Will you help Eduardo up the steps with my chair?'

The manservant hesitated, looking at Rachel still in the back of the car. 'And—the *senhora, senhor?*'

'My wife is feeling a little tired,' said Malcolm, in reply. 'She'll—follow us later. Won't you, Rachel?'

Rachel did not reply. She couldn't. Her heart was pounding so loudly she felt sure it was audible, and she felt physically sick when she thought of what Malcolm was about to do.

Somewhat against his better judgement, the Alejentos' manservant helped Eduardo up the steps with

Malcolm's wheelchair. He was obviously perplexed, in two minds as to whether this was someone he should or should not admit. But Malcolm's attitude was such that he didn't really have much choice in the matter.

Rachel remained where she was. She didn't know what to do. The idea of accompanying Malcolm into the Alejento house did not bear thinking about, but similarly, how could she remain sitting here?

At the top of the steps, Malcolm indicated that Eduardo should take charge of the wheelchair and the manservant led the way into the hall.

Silence fell once more broken only by the birds and the hum of bees among the flowers which grew beside the drive. A somnolent peace descended, but to Rachel it seemed a transitory state. She sat there in the back of the convertible waiting for something to happen, but she didn't know what she expected.

And then the sound of another automobile came to her ears as it accelerated up the drive towards her. It was a red sports car with a young man at the wheel, and beside him sat Amalia Alejento.

Rachel wanted to curl up and die. What would the other girl think when she saw her there? What possible explanation could she give for her presence?

The sports car came to a halt and the young man sprang out looking curiously towards Rachel. As Amalia climbed out too, he said something to her in an undertone and she responded briefly before walking across to the convertible.

'*Bom dia*, Senhora Trevellyan,' she said. 'This is a— surprise!'

Rachel managed a faint smile. 'Yes, isn't it?'

Amalia glanced round as the young man came to join her. 'Allow me to present you to my brother, *senhora*,' she went on. 'Jorge, this is Senhora Trevellyan!'

Jorge Alejento took Rachel's hand courteously and

raised it almost to his lips. '*Muito prazer, senhora*. I am most pleased to make your acquaintance.'

Rachel forced another polite smile, conscious of the admiration in the young man's eyes. She thought he must be about her own age, with sleek dark hair that was cut shorter than Luis's and the same generously-covered bones of his sister.

Amalia's eyes suddenly grew speculative. 'You are here with—the Senhor Marquês, *senhora*?' she questioned sharply.

Rachel shook her head. 'My—my husband wished to see the Marquesa, *senhorita*,' she replied, wishing they would leave her and go on into the building.

Amalia's eyes narrowed now. 'I see. And—the Marquês?'

'As far as I know, he's at the *quinta, senhorita*.'

Amalia nodded, and then looked curiously at her, as though trying to understand why Rachel should not have entered the house with her husband. But fortunately, she decided, or so Rachel assumed, that to ask such a question would be an impertinence unsuited to her station, and with a shrug she gave Rachel a rather patronising smile before beginning to mount the steps.

Half way up she turned, and seeing that her brother was still by the car, said peremptorily: 'Come, Jorge!'

But Jorge Alejento was not so easily controlled. 'You go ahead, Amalia,' he replied lazily, thrusting his hands into his pockets. 'I will stay and keep the *senhora* company for a while.'

'That's not necessary——' began Rachel quickly, but he raised a finger to his lips in a conspiratorial gesture and she halted.

Amalia clicked her tongue, disappearing into the house with obvious reluctance. Clearly she did not like her brother taking an interest in someone whom she regarded with such contempt.

Jorge rested his arms on the top of the car door. 'I have heard about you, *senhora*,' he said, with a lazy smile. 'You are married to this man who has come to stay in Dona Joanna's house, *sim*?'

Rachel moved uncomfortably. 'That's right, *senhor*.'

He nodded slowly. 'This man is confined to a wheel-chair, is he not?'

Rachel moved her head in assent. 'As you say.'

'And he has come here to see Dona Joanna?' Jorge frowned.

'Why don't you go inside and find out for yourself?' Rachel's nerves were stretched and she had no patience with curious youths who thought to entertain themselves by baiting her.

Jorge raised dark eyebrows. 'You think I am being inordinately inquisitive?' He straightened. 'I'm sorry, that was not my intention. It merely stunned me that someone like you should be married to a man old enough to be your father.'

Rachel looked desperately towards the entrance of the house. How much longer was Malcolm going to be?

'Why don't you come inside too?' Jorge was speaking again, and Rachel turned to him irritably.

'I don't wish to enter your home. We were not invited here, and I have no intention of intruding upon your parents' privacy!'

Jorge considered this. 'And your husband, this Senhor Trevellyan. He is intruding?'

'Oh, please. Go away and leave me alone!'

Rachel thrust open the door of the car and stepped out, unable to sit still any longer. It had been bad enough before, but now she was beginning to feel like some peculiar specimen on display. She gave Jorge Alejento a pointed stare and he stepped out of her path, allowing her to cross the forecourt with jerky steps. Oh, why didn't Malcolm come? What was he doing? What was he saying?

'I'm sorry if I've annoyed you, *senhora*.' That was Jorge again. He had followed her and was standing right behind her.

Rachel swung round. 'What do you want of me?' she demanded. 'Why are you doing this? What possible joy can you get from talking to me?'

'Joy, *senhora*? I am afraid I do not understand.'

Rachel made an impatient gesture. 'It means pleasure—satisfaction. What satisfaction does it give you to pester me?'

'Pester, *senhora*?' Jorge tugged at his ear-lobe. 'I'm afraid you've lost me again.'

Unwillingly a smile came to Rachel's lips. It was ridiculous, after all, the whole situation was ridiculous!

She sighed again and looked at the young man more tolerantly. 'How old are you, Jorge?'

Jorge looked taken aback at her casual use of his name. '*Mim!* I am how do you say—twenty and three, *vinte e tres, senhora*.'

'I thought so.' Rachel looked him up and down. 'Go away and find someone else to play with!'

Jorge looked hurt. 'I am not a child, *senhora*.'

'Then stop acting like one. You don't really want to talk to me. You just thought it would be rather an amusing game to stay here and embarrass me with your questions. Well, you don't embarrass me, Jorge, you just annoy me!'

Jorge's face suffused with colour. 'Then I apologise.'

Rachel wrapped her arms about her slim body. 'That's all right.'

'But in any case, you are wrong.'

Rachel turned. 'Why?'

'I admit, my initial intention was to amuse myself

133

for a while. But you interest me. I find your attitude refreshing. I am enjoying talking with you.'

'I don't somehow think your family would approve,' remarked Rachel dryly.

'I am not a child. I am permitted opinions of my own. I was educated in England, and I have talked with English girls before. They are usually more interesting to talk to than Portuguese girls. Here our women are not so emancipated. They confine their conversations to their home and their families. Before they are thirty they are middle-aged and boring!'

Rachel gasped, 'What an indictment!'

'Nevertheless, you will find I am right—except in very special cases. Take my sister Amalia, for example; she has no interests outside the home. She knows how to control servants, run a home efficiently. And no doubt when the time comes that she and Luis have children, she will make a satisfactory mother. But what does she know of the world, of life outside her own narrow little existence? *Nada!* Nothing! She is totally opposed to having to think for herself, to having a career. Can you wonder that an intelligent man finds such a person boring?'

Rachel tried not to be interested, but it was difficult. 'And a man like—like the Marquês: what does he do in such circumstances?'

'If he's bored, you mean?' Jorge frowned.

Rachel made an awkward gesture. 'I suppose so.'

'He finds something—or someone else—to take his interest. Of course, there are some men who find their work a more than adequate substitute for the dissatisfaction of their personal lives.'

Rachel scuffed her sandal against the gravel of the forecourt. 'I think you're only guessing,' she said. 'You don't really know whether you are right. Besides, some men prefer a woman to be wholly subservient to them, to look after their needs and care for their children. To listen when they have something to say. They gain an egotistical satisfaction from being domineering. And in any case, how do you know that Portuguese men are not different from Englishmen in their separate needs? I mean—in England women are reasonably emancipated, I agree, and their husbands appreciate this. It's been a natural progression over the years. But in Portugal women have remained the same for hundreds of years, so perhaps their husbands don't want their wives to become individuals.'

'Men are men, the world over!' exclaimed Jorge forcefully. 'And all men prefer a woman who can entertain their minds as well as their bodies. Just think of Scheherazade!'

Rachel smiled. 'I think that this conversation has gone far enough, Jorge,' she began smilingly, when there was a sudden shout from the doorway of the house behind them.

'*Senhora! Senhora! Venha depressa!*'

Although Rachel wasn't sure what he meant, the urgency in Eduardo's tones was clear enough. Taking a startled look at Jorge, she started across the forecourt, running towards the steps. Jorge ran beside her and when she stumbled he was there to prevent her from falling.

'Oh, thank you,' she gasped, and took the steps two at a time. Then to Eduardo: 'What is it? What's wrong?'

Eduardo let out a stream of incoherent Portuguese that completely confused her. Her knowledge of the language was as yet so slight, and it was obvious in his overwrought state he was unable to speak the few words of English he knew.

But Jorge was there, and Jorge understood Eduardo perfectly. 'He says it is your husband, *senhora*,' he

135

translated. 'He has been—taken ill.'

Rachel's cheeks paled. 'What—*where*?'

Eduardo twisted his hands anxiously. '*Venha comigo, senhora. Por aqui!*'

Jorge put his hand beneath Rachel's elbow and urged her forward. She hardly noticed the panelled hall, or the bowl of mauve, trumpet-shaped flowers that gave off such a delicate perfume. She was conscious only of a sick, frightened feeling in the pit of her stomach, and the nervous anticipation of not knowing what to expect.

Eduardo showed them into a room which seemed small compared to the rooms at the Quinta Martinez, but which was nevertheless a comfortable apartment. The room seemed full of people, and perhaps that was why it seemed smaller still, and Rachel's eyes sped swiftly round the group of strangely silent faces, searching for her husband's. And then she realised he was lying on a couch in the middle of the floor, and that someone, a man, was kneeling beside him, pressing his ear to Malcolm's chest.

Rachel shook off Jorge's restraining hand and ran forward, dropping to her knees beside the couch, taking Malcolm's hand, trying to tell herself that he was merely unconscious. His eyes were closed, one side of his face was hideously twisted, he didn't seem to be breathing!

The man rose to his feet, shaking his head helplessly. Rachel looked up at him, realising he must be Senhor Alejento. He had the same features as his son, and as Rachel had been so recently talking to his son, she recognised him at once.

She moved her head slowly from side to side and then looked back disbelievingly at her husband. 'Is—is he dead?' she breathed in horror.

'I am afraid so, *senhora*.' Senhor Alejento spoke

stiffly and without emotion. 'It was very quick. There was nothing we could do.'

'No!' Rachel shook her head more quickly. 'No, I don't believe you. How—how can he be dead? He—he was perfectly all right half an hour ago!' Her voice had risen as she spoke, and now she got to her feet, staring round at them wildly. 'What happened here? Why is he dead? What have you done to him?'

'He was an *evil* man!'

It was the Marquesa de Mendao who had spoken, and Rachel swung round to confront her. She was standing beside another woman whom Rachel realised must be Senhora Alejento, who was supporting her with a comforting arm. The Marquesa looked ill, but Rachel could not feel pity.

'How can you say that?' she demanded tremulously. 'You—the Trevellyans took you in—they—they cared for you!'

The Marquesa moved her shoulders wearily. 'You don't know anything about it, *senhora*. Your husband came here to—to——' She broke off. 'If he is dead, he has no one to blame but himself.'

Rachel stared at them all: at the Marquesa, leaning heavily on Senhora Alejento, so cold and unfeeling both of them in their silent condemnation. She looked at Senhor Alejento, and Amalia, who looked frozen, her calm features belying an inner torment, but why?

She looked at Eduardo, realising his horror at his part in the proceedings. No doubt he was already anticipating Luis's anger when he discovered Eduardo was responsible for bringing them here. And finally she looked at Jorge Alejento, the only person in the room who seemed concerned about her.

She drew a trembling breath. It was suddenly very hot in here. She could hardly get her breath. The atmosphere was so tangible, she felt she could have cut it with a knife. It was a pressing, hostile atmosphere, and an unreasoning sense of panic rose inside her. This couldn't actually be happening, it just *couldn't*! Malcolm wasn't dead, he was alive, demanding, aggressive, not cold and still and lifeless.

She raised a confused hand to her forehead and found it was damp. She was sweating, but why? She felt cold, very cold. Her breathing was quickening, and she didn't know why. Was nobody going to say anything? Was nobody going to express pity at the passing of a human being?

She looked again at Jorge. His eyes were full of compassion. With a helpless gesture she tried to move towards him, but her legs felt leaden, they wouldn't move. Her panic increased. An encroaching blackness was colouring the outer reaches of her brain. It was difficult to think, to move, to breathe...

A sob rose in her throat, but it was never emitted. Instead, she sank with a faint sigh, unconscious at their feet.

CHAPTER NINE

THE exact sequence of events of the next few days were never afterwards very clear in Rachel's mind, although at the time they seemed acutely memorable. She was consumed with a sense of guilt, doubtful that had she accompanied Malcolm into the Alejento house this terrible thing would have occurred. She blamed herself for abandoning him, and would not listen to that inner voice which continually reminded her that Malcolm's motives for going to Alcorado were not admirable ones. The Marquesa had not enlarged on her initial outburst just after Malcolm's fatal stroke, but it was obvious that there had been some kind of confrontation. Even so, it was difficult to feel anything but guilt when grief seemed so elusive.

There were times, of course, when a certain nostalgia overwhelmed her; but that was all it was, and when she recalled Malcolm's treatment of her father and more lately of herself, bitterness choked her throat.

She had recovered consciousness in one of the bedrooms of the house. There had been a maid stationed beside her bed, and Jorge Alejento had been hovering by the door. She had come round with a distinct feeling of foreboding which had increased when full consciousness brought full recall.

Jorge had explained that Luis had been contacted, and that he was already on his way to take charge of the situation. By the time Luis arrived Rachel was downstairs again, pale but composed, scarcely able to accept the situation even then.

Luis came straight to the *sala* where Rachel was waiting for him. Senhora Alejento was seated with her, but she might as well have been alone, for the *senhora* had not spoken a word.

She didn't know what explanations had been made to him, but Luis asked no awkward questions about why they should be at Alcorado in the first place, and merely enquired how she was feeling. His eyes mirrored a little of the concern of Jorge's. Clearly, in spite of his mother's involvement, he could not dismiss death so cold-bloodedly.

Then he went away again, and something inside her froze. What was she going to do? What did one do in circumstances like these? Would Malcolm's body have to be transported back to England for burial? Her mind shied away from the thought. If only there was someone she could have contacted back home, some relative perhaps who would come here and take charge of everything. But there was no one.

Senhora Alejento sat very still. Rachel had never known such a *still* person. In her black morning dress, her dark hair smoothed into a chignon, she was immaculately groomed, her face bearing little expression. Surely she ought to say something, thought Rachel, a trifle hysterically. In similar circumstances she would have wanted to console the bereaved wife, not treat her like some particularly obnoxious creature who just happened to be present at this most inconvenient time. Were all this family like that? Senhor Alejento; Amalia! She came to Jorge, and unwillingly a sense of warmth invaded her chilled limbs. He was not like the others. He had warmth, and understanding; a sense of humour. Oh, yes, a sense of humour was so important even in terrible circumstances like these. She looked at Senhora Alejento's stiff, unyielding features and a hiccough of suppressed laughter broke from her. How silly this was, sitting here, not speaking, not moving, acting like corpses themselves. But they were not dead;

140

it was Malcolm who was dead; Malcolm who was lying so stiff and unmoving in that other room.

She giggled, and the sound echoed round the quiet room. Senhora Alejento turned her head to look at Rachel with cold, disapproving eyes, and Rachel laughed again. She went on laughing. It *was* funny, she thought wildly, very funny.

Senhora Alejento moved then, quickly. She hurried across the room to summon assistance and reached the door just as Luis burst through it. For once he was without his courtliness. He didn't apologise for almost knocking the *senhora* over, but went straight to Rachel and slapped her face hard.

Her laughter subsided as quickly as it had begun, and she gazed up at him with a pained expression. 'You—you hit me!' she exclaimed tremulously.

'I had to.' Luis glanced round impatiently and saw Senhora Alejento watching them from the doorway. 'Look—please, calm yourself! We will be leaving very shortly.'

'Leaving?' Rachel was puzzled. 'Leaving for where?'

'The *quinta*, of course.' Luis had a muscle jerking in his temple. 'The arrangements are almost complete. Wait only a few minutes more.'

'And—and Malcolm?' Rachel felt a lump in her throat.

'Rest assured, everything is being dealt with—er—*senhora*!'

Rachel was sure he had added that final appellation for Senhora Alejento's benefit. She was watching their interchange closely and Rachel realised that at no time had she addressed him in any formal way. But this wasn't the time to be remembering those sort of things. They were not important. Malcolm's death had proved how transitory a thing life could be. What was important was trying to assimilate her position now.

She would be returning to England, of course, and somehow she had to accept that from now on she would be on her own.

'You will be all right now, *senhora*?'

Luis was speaking again, and Rachel nodded. 'Of course,' she answered dully, 'Senhor Marquês!'

Luis looked at her for a long moment, his expression enigmatic, and then without another word he turned and left the room. After he had gone, Senhora Alejento closed the door again and came back to her seat. But now she seemed disposed to talk, for she said:

'You will be returning to England soon, *senhora*. No doubt you will be glad to do so.'

Rachel hesitated. Would she be glad? Of course she would, she told herself vehemently. There was nothing for her here. England at least was her homeland, and although she had no relatives she had some good friends in Mawvry.

Forcing a calmness she did not feel, she replied: 'I expect I shall be leaving very soon. Tomorrow, perhaps.'

'Of course.' Her reply seemed to satisfy the *senhora*. 'You are young, *senhora*. Perhaps you will marry again.'

Rachel felt a sense of distaste. 'I don't think that's at all likely. Besides, this is neither the time nor the place to discuss such a thing,' she declared.

'Why not?' Senhora Alejento's mouth assumed a haughty slant. 'One must be practical, and surely your husband's death cannot have been wholly surprising. He was not a young man, and he had been very ill, had he not?'

Rachel got to her feet and wandered restlessly about the room. She didn't want to talk to this cold woman. She wished Luis would hurry back.

'It is as well it happened now,' went on Senhora Ale-

142

jento. 'It would have been most unpleasant if your husband had still been here at the time of Amalia and Luis's marriage. It could so easily have interfered with their arrangements, and after all, your husband was no relation, was he? No relation whatsoever.'

Rachel clenched her hands. 'I'd rather not discuss my husband with you, *senhora*,' she said tautly.

'Why not?' Senhora Alejento raised her dark brows. 'Surely you are aware that your presence at the *quinta* was an embarrassment to the Marquesa!'

Rachel stared at the other woman with dislike. 'Then she should not have invited my husband there!'

'I cannot imagine why she did. She regretted it the moment it was done.'

Rachel was about to make some rejoinder when the door opened again and Luis reappeared. She stood where she was, in the middle of the floor, and looked at him, and he said: 'Come! We are returning to the *quinta* at once.'

Senhora Alejento rose to her feet. 'Everything is arranged, Luis?' she queried.

'I believe so, Dona Manuela.'

'Where is Amalia?'

'In her room, I think. I have not seen her within the last half hour.'

'You will see her before you go?' The *senhora* frowned.

'Of course.' Luis clicked his heels politely. '*Senhora!*'

Rachel realised he meant her and with reluctant steps she preceded him out of the door. She did not look at Senhora Alejento. She had nothing more to say to her.

In the hall the Marquesa and Sara Ribialto awaited them. Obviously they were returning to the *quinta*, too, for their luggage was beside them. The Marquesa gave Rachel a dispassionate stare, and Rachel looked away from that cold appraisal. The Marquesa seemed to have herself well in hand now and no doubt regretted her momentary loss of control.

Outside the blue convertible stood unattended while Luis opened the door of the silver-grey limousine which he had used to bring them from the airport two weeks ago. Rachel looked round, then her brow furrowed. Where was Malcolm's body?

As though sensing her silent question, Luis came behind her and said: 'I have made arrangements with a firm of *agentes de funerais, senhora*. Your husband will return to the *quinta* later.'

Rachel looked up at him with agonised eyes, and the Marquesa stepped forward. 'Is that necessary, Luis?' she asked, through tight lips. 'Would it not be more sensible to have—arrangements made at the airport? For tomorrow?'

'Tomorrow?' Luis frowned. 'What is to happen tomorrow?'

Rachel knew what the Marquesa was meaning, and she was pretty sure Luis knew it, too. But he wasn't going to help his mother in that respect.

She sighed, twisting her lace gloves. 'Luis, you know perfectly well that—that Senhora Trevellyan will be returning to England tomorrow. She has arrangements to make, funeral arrangements. She cannot afford to waste even a day. You must know that.'

Luis's mouth was a thin line. 'On the contrary, Mama, Senhora Trevellyan needs time to decide what to do. It would not be feasible to fly her home tomorrow——'

'Why not? I'm sure—Malcolm would want to be buried in Cornwall.'

'Does it matter where he is buried?' Luis spoke grimly. 'Mama, I do not think we should act hastily. Surely you must realise the *senhora* has had a terrible

144

shock. She is not fit to deal with funeral arrangements!'

'Oh, really, I can manage——' Rachel began desperately. She must not get involved in a quarrel between the Marquesa and her son. The Marquesa was right; it would be best for her to leave immediately. Tonight, if possible. Although the prospect of returning to that bleak house on the Cornish cliffs with only Malcolm's body for company was terrifying right at this moment. Oh, she *must* pull herself together!

'You see,' the Marquesa was saying triumphantly to her son, 'Senhora Trevellyan would prefer to go home! Of course she would. No doubt she has relatives there——'

'She has no one, Mama,' stated Luis categorically.

'How do you know that?' The Marquesa's small hands were almost tearing the lace gloves to shreds.

'Her husband told me,' replied Luis distinctly. 'Now, will you get in the car, Mama?'

Rachel was still puzzling over how Luis should know that she had no relatives when goodbyes had been said and the sleek silver limousine was cruising smoothly down the drive. She had been installed in the front passenger seat, beside Luis, while his mother occupied the back with Sara Ribialto.

The atmosphere before they left had been disturbingly hostile. Both Senhor and Senhora Alejento appeared to agree with the Marquesa that it was foolish having Malcolm's body transported to the *quinta*, and Amalia when she appeared looked pale and strained.

Rachel felt dreadful about the whole affair, but Luis would listen to no objections from her. He had taken charge completely, and just now she did not have the strength to gainsay him.

It was late afternoon when they arrived back at the *quinta* and Rachel realised the faintness she was feeling was partially due to the fact that she had eaten nothing since breakfast. But in spite of her condition, the idea of food was anathema to her.

It was peculiar travelling up the thickly wooded drive of the *quinta*, and to see the turreted outline of the building appearing through the trees. She felt a strange sense of homecoming, which was ridiculous in the circumstances, unless it was that the Alejento house had become such a cold and alien place to her. In any event, soon she would be on her way back to England, so there was no point in seeing the *quinta* as a refuge now.

The car halted at the foot of the steps leading up to the terrace. Rachel got out immediately, without assistance, but Luis helped the Marquesa and she mounted the steps stiffly. Momentarily Rachel wondered where Eduardo could be, and then realised he would be returning home with Malcolm's body. There would be the coffin that Luis had arranged to pay for, and she felt a twinge of alarm. Did Malcolm have any insurance for an event like this? There were so many things to think about when someone died, and her head began to ache when she tried to think coherently.

Mario and Luisa had both appeared on the terrace to welcome home their mistress, but Rachel still stood beside the car feeling actually physically sick. Luis, who had begun to follow the others, turned and saw her there, and came back to her.

'What's wrong?' he asked, and the gentleness in his voice was her undoing. She shook her head and turned away, huge tears overspilling her eyes and running helplessly down her cheeks. She rubbed her cheeks furiously with the palms of her hands, but he came round her and saw what she was doing.

'Oh, Rachel,' he exclaimed huskily, 'don't cry. Let's go into the house.'

146

But once she had started it was not so easy to stop, and she dragged a tissue out of her handbag and rubbed her eyes. She was aware of the Marquesa turning to see what was going on, and Luis, who put an arm around her shoulders and urged her up the steps, gave his mother an impatient look.

'Luis——' she began, but he shook his head.

'Not now, Mama.'

'But, Luis——' The Marquesa sounded angry.

'I said not now, Mama,' returned Luis forcefully, and escorted Rachel along the corridor to her own suite of rooms.

She was glad he did not take her to Malcolm's rooms. It was too soon to go in there and begin the terrible task of packing his things away.

In her rooms, Luis released her and stood silently by the door.

'You are hungry,' he said. 'I will arrange for Rosa to bring you something.'

'No! No, don't do that,' Rachel sniffed, trying to compose herself. 'I—I'm not hungry.'

'But you must eat!' Luis was impatient. 'You are already much too thin. You cannot afford to neglect yourself.'

Rachel bent her head. 'There—there are matters we must discuss,' she said, ignoring his outburst. 'About travelling home——'

'They can wait!' Luis was arrogant.

'But they can't.' Rachel looked up at him. 'Don't you see? I've got to take charge of everything now. There is no one else.'

'In England? I know that.'

'You said that before. How do you know?'

'Your husband told me.'

Rachel tried to assimilate this. 'Malcolm? But why should he tell you a thing like that?'

Luis thrust his hands into his trousers pockets, tautening the cloth across his thighs. 'He told me when he was explaining how he came to marry you.'

Rachel quivered, forcing down the familiar feeling of sickness she always felt when she considered that particular period of her life. 'I see.' She would have liked to have asked him exactly what Malcolm had said by way of an explanation, but of course she couldn't. 'Well, anyway, there is no one——'

'I said there was no one in England. I am here.'

Rachel blinked. 'What do you mean?'

'I shall take charge of everything for you. Malcolm can be buried here, in Mendao. There is no reason for you to return to England until after the funeral.'

'Oh, but I—I couldn't do that——'

'Why not?'

She shook her head. 'There—there's the money to consider——'

He frowned. 'That need not worry you.'

'Of course it must.' Rachel linked and unlinked her fingers. 'I have to go home and see Malcolm's solicitors —to find out what I must do——'

'You can do that afterwards.'

Rachel moved restlessly about the room, unable to hold his penetrating stare. She tugged at a strand of her hair which seemed too weighty for the slenderness of her neck, and moved her head in a confused way. 'But—your mother——' she began unhappily.

'I am master here, not my mother.'

Rachel sighed. 'What about—the Alejentos; Amalia?'

As she said the other girl's name she coloured. Amalia was Senhorita Alejento to her!

But Luis seemed unconcerned. 'Amalia has nothing to do with this. She will agree with me.'

Rachel spread her hands. 'I—I don't know what to do.'

'Then leave it to me.'

She looked tremulously at him. 'I wish I could!'

Luis took a step towards her and then halted. 'You can, and you know it,' he said, in a strangely hoarse voice.

Rachel turned away. 'All right, if you say so.' The trembling feeling inside her was increasing and nausea was threatening to overwhelm her. If he didn't hurry up and leave her she would disgrace herself completely by being sick right there in front of him. 'If—if you'll —excuse me——'

She walked blindly towards the bathroom door and Luis had perforce to let her go. She heard his footsteps recede along the corridor as she leant weakly against the cool wall of the bathroom. How long, she wondered despairingly, would it take her to begin to feel normal again?

Malcolm was buried the following afternoon in the graveyard beside the small church down in the village.

It was a Catholic burial, and Malcolm had not been a Catholic. But as he had had no religious affiliations whatsoever, Rachel didn't think he would mind.

Despite the unexpectedness of the occasion, it was not the insignificant little affair Rachel had imagined. The Alejentos were there in force, and Luis's estate managers and their wives, as well as the Marquesa, Rachel, and Luis himself. Of course, she realised, the fact that the Marquês de Mendao was involved counted for something, and that, no doubt, was why the villagers turned out in force to see the procession and to hear the Mass.

Rachel had been doubtful about what to wear. There was nothing black in her wardrobe, and as the women round here wore black or some other dark colour almost without relief, there was no doubt that something similar was required, but what? Apart from a pair of black trousers, she had nothing. Then Rosa came to the rescue.

She came into Rachel's bedroom as she was looking hopelessly through the few garments she had, and said: 'You wish something for the funeral, *senhora*?'

'Oh, yes, Rosa!' Rachel turned to her. 'Is there anywhere that I could buy a dark dress?'

'Not in Mendao, *senhora*. But I could—how do you say it—lend you a dress, if you would permit me?'

'Could you? Could you really? Oh, Rosa, that would be marvellous!' Rachel closed her wardrobe door. 'Anything would do. A black skirt, a dress—I can hardly wear trousers, can I?'

'*Nao, senhora*. A moment. I will not be long.'

When Rosa came back she was carrying a plain black dress not unlike the one she was wearing at the moment. Rachel stripped off her jeans and sweater and tried it on. It was very long compared to the dresses she was used to wearing, several inches below her knees, in fact, and because Rosa was of a more generous build it hung on Rachel's thin shoulders. Nevertheless it was exactly what she wanted, and she thanked the other girl warmly.

The funeral was to take place in the late afternoon and Rachel spent some time over her appearance. She wanted to do the right thing. She wanted to look suitable for once in her life.

But when Luis came along to her rooms to tell her it was time to leave he stared in horror at the shapeless black dress and severely styled hair. He was looking particularly immaculate in a dark, pin-striped suit, and she felt very much the poor relation.

'*Meu Deus!*' he breathed, shaking his head. 'What

have you done to yourself?'

Rachel coloured. 'I borrowed this dress from Rosa, Isn't it—suitable?'

Luis rested one hand against the back of his neck, over the thick black hair. 'It does not even fit you.'

'I know. But it does—cover me, doesn't it?'

'Indeed.' His tone was dry. 'But come! There is no time to change now. My mother is awaiting us.'

The Marquesa's expression when she saw Rachel was pained. Her narrowed eyes flickered over the girl with obvious distaste, and she quickly looked away without making any comment. In a slim-fitting two-piece of black silk, and a black straw boater, like her son she was coolly elegant, and Rachel fumbled for the black chiffon scarf Rosa had lent her for her hair.

Fortunately for Rachel, the poignancy of the occasion was sufficient to strip her of any sense of humiliation, and not until Malcolm's body had been interred and they were back at the *quinta* did she again become conscious of her appearance. Then she left the others as soon as they entered the coolness of the hall, hurrying back to the privacy of her rooms.

But on impulse, she stopped at the door to the suite of rooms Malcolm had occupied and turning the handle, pushed it wide.

In spite of everything that had happened, it was a strange experience to find the rooms empty, the bedroom visible through an open door. She stepped forward into the *sala* and ran her finger lightly over the back of the leather couch. It was cool to the touch and she walked slowly to the french doors and pushed one open. Beyond, the patio was empty. The glass-topped table and loungers had gone, and there was a curiously desolate air about it.

A lump rose in her throat. Already the *quinta* had shed all trace of Malcolm's presence. He might never have been here. And pretty soon now her rooms would look like this.

'*Senhora!*'

The voice behind her was sudden and unexpected. She turned to face the speaker reluctantly. 'Yes, Senhora Marquesa?' she responded politely.

'May I speak with you for a moment?'

Rachel shrugged. 'If you like.'

'It's about—it's about your leaving here, *senhora*.'

Rachel had thought it might be. 'Yes?'

'Have you discussed your plans with my son?'

'I haven't actually made any plans yet, Senhora Marquesa.'

'Don't you think you should?'

'I intend to. It's just that—well, it's all been so sudden. I don't think I've really accepted the situation yet.'

'Oh, nonsense!' The Marquesa's mouth was tight. 'You must have had some thoughts on the future. You know you can't stay here.'

'Yes, I do know that. It may interest you to know, Senhora Marquesa, that I have no wish to remain here!'

The Marquesa stiffened. 'Good. I shall tell my son you wish to leave as soon as possible.'

'Yes, you do that.' Rachel's nails dug into the palms of her hands.

The Marquesa looked about her. 'By the way, your husband's belongings have been packed into his suitcase and are ready when you want them.'

'I could have done that,' said Rachel quickly, disliking the idea of a stranger disposing of Malcolm's things. 'Is that all?'

'I think so——'

'What is going on here, Mama?'

Luis had come to stand just behind his mother and

152

she turned to him with a faint smile. 'Nothing is—going on, Luis. Senhora Trevellyan and I were merely discussing when she planned to leave.'

Luis stepped into the room. 'Is that important at the moment?' he demanded. '*Valha-me Deus*, give the girl a chance! We only buried her husband an hour ago!'

His mother's expression froze. 'Luis, are you aware that there are less than eight weeks left to your wedding? There is still a lot to be done, you know that. How can you possibly behave so casually? It's obvious that the Alejentos are becoming concerned at your attitude——'

'A few days more or less will not create too many difficulties, Mama. Besides, everything is in hand and you know it. You are merely using this as a lever——'

'Oh, please!' Rachel wanted to be the cause of no more argument between Luis and his mother. 'I want to leave! If it's at all possible I'd like to go tomorrow.'

Luis turned to her then. 'You are not fit to return to England—to cope with dozens of finalising details. I have already contacted my own solicitor in Coimbra and he is arranging to have a representative sent to England to take charge of your affairs. You have only to instruct him and your wishes will be carried out.'

'And—and what am I to do in the meantime?' asked Rachel faintly.

'You are to stay here, of course. A couple of weeks of complete rest and relaxation will do you the world of good. Then—and only then—will you be fit enough to take charge of your own affairs again.'

'*No!*' The Marquesa pressed a hand to her breast, staring at her son as if she couldn't believe her ears. 'I won't allow it!'

'*You* won't allow it?' Luis's eyes were cold as he stared at his mother, and Rachel felt terrible.

'There's no need for you to get upset, Senhora Marquesa,' she exclaimed. 'I—I—I shan't be staying!'

Luis turned back to her. 'Why not?'

'You ask me that!' Rachel spread her hands. 'Oh, just go—both of you! Go away and leave me alone!'

Luis was breathing heavily, and his mother was clearly bereft of words for the first time in her life. Rachel turned away. It was horrible when someone disliked you as much as the Marquesa apparently disliked her. And why? Because she had come here with Malcolm, and dared to upset her carefully laid plans. She would be glad to get away, she told herself fiercely. Better to be alone and independent than here where her presence created such open conflict.

'*Senhora!*'

That was Luis, his voice harsh and aggressive. He was glaring at her now, and she knew that had his mother not been there he would have said much more.

'I'm sorry.' Rachel bent her head. 'Thank you for your—your offer, but I have to go.'

Luis stared at her impotently for several seconds and then he turned and strode out of the room. After he had gone there was silence and Rachel looked expressively at the Marquesa, expecting her to go, too. But the older woman stood her ground.

'Thank you, *senhora,*' she said, at last.

Rachel was taken aback. 'For what?'

'For refusing my son's invitation.'

Rachel frowned. 'You don't have to thank me.'

'Oh, but I do. You could so easily have accepted.'

'I think not.' Rachel wished she would go. She wanted nothing from this arrogant old woman.

The Marquesa half turned and then halted. 'You know, if—if there is any way in which I can help you financially, *senhora*——'

'No, thank you.' Rachel spoke bitterly. 'I'm not like Malcolm. I don't want your money!'

The Marquesa went pale. 'Why do you say that? What do you—that is——' She broke off. 'My offer was made in good faith, *senhora*.'

'Oh, was it?' Rachel drew a heavy breath. 'Well, all I want is to be left alone.'

The Marquesa took a couple of steps and then halted again. 'You wouldn't—I mean——' She bit her lower lip. 'What—what will you do?'

'In England, you mean?' Rachel shrugged. 'I'm not sure. Paint again, perhaps. Who knows? I might make a success of it.'

'If you would care to send some of your work to me, I would see whether I could help you,' volunteered the Marquesa.

Rachel frowned. 'Why should you do that?' Then, with a shrug: 'Anyway, I don't want your help. There's no way you can help me.'

The Marquesa looked strained. 'I see.'

'And now, if you've nothing more to say, I'd like to be alone. I—I have some packing to do.'

The Marquesa moved slowly out into the corridor. Her shoulders sagged, and she looked somehow defeated. Rachel couldn't understand why. Surely she was doing what the Marquesa wanted. She followed her to the door and watched as the older woman went along the corridor. The sooner she got away from the *quinta* the better, for all their sakes.

And yet, in spite of this conviction, the idea of returning to England and never seeing Luis again was desolating.

CHAPTER TEN

RACHEL returned to England the day after Malcolm's funeral.

She had refused to listen to Luis when he again appealed to her to remain in Mendao while his representative dealt with her affairs, although she could not prevent him from instructing his solicitors to handle all the legal details on her behalf.

Instead, much to his mother's relief, she felt, she left the beauty of the Portuguese *quinta* and travelled home to the lonely unattractive house on the cliffs where Malcolm Trevellyan had spent most of his adult life.

She took a taxi from the railway station to Mawvry, and after the driver had deposited her and her luggage on the doorstep he drove away again, leaving her feeling more alone than she had ever felt.

But perhaps it was that very knowledge that she had now to be mistress of her own affairs which gave her the strength to do what had to be done. Her initial desire to lock up the house and move into the village inn was squashed by simple economics, for she realised that very probably this big house would have to be sold soon, and she had no idea how many debts Malcolm might have run up. And there was still the funeral expenses to consider.

All the same, it was a lonely mausoleum for one person, and those first few nights brought a series of terrifying nightmares in which her dead husband was the central character. She would awake sweating, to find everything was calm and still, but without being able to get back to sleep again.

Of course, Luis himself was responsible for no small part of that insomnia. She thought of him too often and too much, and she was relieved she had had the sense to leave Mendao before something disastrous happened.

Not that she ever fooled herself that Luis might have broken his betrothal to Amalia for her. On the contrary, she knew that for him to do such a thing would be against every dictate of the society he lived in and respected. But he was attracted to her, that much even she knew, and she was very much afraid that given the time and persuasion, she might have been tempted to take any small crumb he was prepared to offer.

The village people were very kind. She realised that to them Malcolm's death was in many ways a release, for they knew that she would never treat them as he had done. All the same, Rachel wondered what would happen, and felt a sense of revulsion at taking Malcolm's place. She didn't really want this house or his money, if there was any money to be had, and she began thinking of ways in which she might get a place of her own and earn her own living.

It was several days before she could bring herself to go through Malcolm's personal papers.

She had contacted Malcolm's solicitors, of course, the day after her return to England, and given the name of Valmez and Franca, Luis's solicitors. She explained that they would deal with all the legal details on her behalf and was glad of the release this gave her.

But to go through the small deed box which Malcolm had always kept locked in his wardrobe, that was something only she could do, and she realised that sooner or later the solicitors would want to know what it contained.

She didn't know why she should have such an aversion to going through Malcolm's personal things. After all, they were only lifeless scraps of paper. There could be nothing of value there. His will had been deposited with his solicitors, they had told her that, and what little money he had had been in the bank books which he had taken to Portugal with him.

When she first opened the deed box she sat back on her heels in surprise. She had expected to find only one or two items inside. Instead, what she found was a box full of letters and papers.

It took her no time to realise that these were the letters Malcolm had received periodically from Joanna Martinez. There were quite a lot of them, but Rachel had no desire to read what the Marquesa had written.

Instead, she concentrated on the other items. There was Malcolm's birth certificate and their marriage certificate; some old photographs and insurance policies, and some papers which bore the name of Elizabeth Trevellyan, who Rachel knew had been Malcolm's mother. There didn't appear to be anything of any importance, and Rachel was loath to explore further. She was about to close the box again when she caught sight of another certificate which was protruding from the papers she had examined which had borne Malcolm's mother's name.

Curiously, she picked it up, expecting it to be Elizabeth Trevellyan's birth certificate or perhaps her marriage certificate. But it was neither. It was a birth certificate, certainly, but it bore the name of Joanna Portreath.

Rachel was astonished. The mother's name was there, someone called Rosemary Portreath, but the father's name was unknown. The date of birth was the seventeenth of August, 1914.

Rachel got to her feet and stared at the certificate in

dismay. The name, the date of birth, everything fitted. This had to be Joanna Martinez's birth certificate.

For several minutes she just stood there, looking at the slip of paper in her hand, trying to assimilate what this meant. Who was Rosemary Portreath, that was what she had to find out now.

Dropping to her knees again, she riffled through the papers. Impatiently she opened old insurance policies, savings certificates, photographs that meant nothing to her whatsoever.

And then she came upon it. The thing she had unknowingly been seeking: Malcolm's mother's birth certificate. And there it was: plain for anyone to see. Elizabeth, daughter of Amos and Naomi Portreath. This Rosemary Portreath must have been Elizabeth's sister.

Rachel tried to think. If Rosemary was Elizabeth's sister, then that made Malcolm and Joanna cousins. She frowned. But Malcolm had said Joanna was orphaned and his parents had cared for her. Still, that was possible. If Joanna's mother had died, she would be orphaned because her parents were not married; she had no father!

Rachel caught her breath on a gasp. Now she was beginning to understand. This birth certificate was the real link between Malcolm and Joanna, the thing which had coloured their relationship.

But why? Rachel asked herself. What use had Malcolm had for such an ancient document? What possible reason was there for him to have kept it all this time? Surely it was Joanna's property.

She bit hard at her lower lip. Of course, the inevitable answers presented themselves. In his dealings with her father, Malcolm had not been above blackmail, and this—this was something explosive!

She thought of the Marquesa, so strict and correct;

to imagine her horror at being exposed as illegitimate did not bear thinking about.

But the more Rachel thought about it, the more convinced she became that she was right. So many things fitted into place, not least their acceptance into the Martinez household.

But did Luis know? That was the question. Somehow she doubted it. She doubted whether he would submit to threats as easily as his mother, if indeed that was the case.

She paced restlessly about the bedroom. How long had Malcolm known the secret of his cousin's birth? How long had the birth certificate been in his hands? Surely he could not have been blackmailing her for forty years!

Thrusting the certificate aside, Rachel went down on her knees beside the box again and began taking out the letters. They were still in their envelopes in most cases and she was able to read the postmarks on some of them. The earliest date she could find was a little over four years old. She frowned. Malcolm's mother had died four years ago. It all fitted. That must have been when the birth certificate fell into Malcolm's hands.

Rachel dropped the letters as if they had burned her. So many things were falling into place, not least being the Marquesa's attitude the day of the funeral. Her words about helping Rachel assumed a different appearance. How she had looked when Rachel had said she was not like Malcolm! Did she think—could she possibly imagine that she, Rachel, knew of Malcolm's treachery?

Rachel felt sick. The whole thing appalled her, but what could she do?

And then she saw something else at the bottom of the box. It was black, and when she drew it out she found it was a bank book. She turned it over in her fingers curiously. She had thought Malcolm was a member of only one bank, and not this one.

With trembling fingers she opened the book, and then she gasped in horror. Far from being short of money as Malcolm had always maintained he was, the contents of the book revealed that he had almost ten thousand pounds deposited. Ten thousand pounds! But how?

She turned the pages, and then everything became clear. There were regular deposits of two hundred pounds every month made over a period of over three years.

Rachel was horrified. This then was the man who had pretended an affection for the Marquesa, who had insinuated himself into her house when he thought his chances of bleeding her dry were escaping him.

Rachel got to her feet again and heaved a deep sigh. She needed a cup of tea. Anything to take the horrible taste of blackmail out of her mouth.

Downstairs in the kitchen, she sipped the scalding liquid, trying to think coherently. What now? What ought she to do? If she sent the certificate to the Marquesa, would that exonerate her from all blame? And what did one do about transferring such a large amount of money out of the country? Because that was what she would have to do. It was the Marquesa's money and she wanted none of it.

She sighed. If only there was someone to whom she could turn, someone to whom she could confide the ugly aspects of the situation. But there was no one. If she told the solicitors what she suspected, there might have to be a court case, and the last thing she wanted for this was publicity. The Marquesa had suffered all these years, living in fear of exposure. To reveal everything now would mean that those years of agony had been in vain. No, Rachel could not do that, not even to the woman who had treated her with such contempt. And maybe she had had some justification, Rachel conceded now. If she had believed that Rachel was a party to the conspiracy ...

It was early evening, and on impulse Rachel slipped on a cardigan and went for a walk on the cliffs. She needed to get away from the house, from the pervading influence of her dead husband, so that she could seriously consider what to do.

It was a beautiful evening, cool and fresh, with only a faint drift of cloud on the horizon. Spring was here and everything was burgeoning with new life. It was the time of year Rachel liked most and she thought with sudden longing of her oils and canvas. It seemed years, not just weeks, since she had picked up her brush and lost herself in the simple enjoyment of her work.

It was dark when she finally returned to the house. She went straight upstairs and pushed everything back into the deed box again and then thrust it out of sight in the wardrobe. Downstairs, she breathed deeply. She would forget about it for the moment, she told herself determinedly. If she hadn't seen the birth certificate she would never have learnt the truth, and it was certain that no solicitor knew of the deed box's existence.

Malcolm's affairs took some time to tie up, but Rachel didn't mind. She was told that the house would be hers, but there was very little money and it was doubtful that she would be able to afford to keep it on. The cottages Malcolm had owned in the village had only very small rents, and as he had refused to do any repairs he had had no opportunity to raise them. And it was certain that Rachel would not now be able to afford repairs. She refused to consider touching the money in the bank book in the deed box.

So the cottages were sold, in some cases to their tenants at a quarter their value. The solicitors thought she was mad, allowing the chance for obtaining a small nest-egg to slip through her fingers, but Rachel thought it was the least she could do for people who for years had had to put up with Malcolm's meanness.

She had begun painting again, and although she sometimes found it difficult to concentrate, it nevertheless provided the outlet she needed.

The days slid into weeks and the weather grew warmer. Tourists began coming to Mawvry and Rachel left the isolation of the house on the cliffs to mix more freely with her friends in the village. She was just beginning to feel normal again, her longing to see Luis dulled to a heavy ache in the region of her heart.

Occasionally she would awaken in the early hours of the morning and find herself calculating how many more weeks it was to his wedding, but at night she made sure she was physically exhausted when she went to bed and usually fell asleep quite quickly.

She thought she was losing a little weight and this troubled her sometimes. Since her marriage to Malcolm she had never had much flesh on her bones, but now they seemed to protrude through her tanned skin, her wrists particularly appearing veined and fragile.

And then, one morning, there was a letter.

She picked it up from the mat carelessly, expecting it to be from the solicitor, only to find it had a Portuguese postmark.

Immediately her heart began pounding and there was a weakness in her lower limbs. She carried the letter into the kitchen and forced herself to put on the kettle before attempting to open it. It was from the Marquesa, and between the folded page was a cheque which fluttered unheeded to the floor.

My dear Senhora Trevellyan, the Marquesa had written, *I am enclosing a small gift which I trust you will use to your best advantage. Accept it as a token of my appreciation. Yours sincerely, Joanna Martinez.*

Rachel bent and lifted the cheque with some distaste. What was this supposed to mean? Why was the Marquesa thanking her? For what?

The cheque was for forty thousand escudos, and Rachel's mind reeled. *Forty thousand escudos!* How much was that in pounds and pence? She shook her head. It didn't matter how much it was for; it would have to go back. She wanted nothing from the Marquesa.

She made her tea in a daze, trying desperately to understand why the Marquesa should have thought it necessary to send her money. And then she thought she knew. The Marquesa had waited to hear from her. She had not believed her when she had said she was not like Malcolm. All this time the old lady must have been waiting for the demands to begin and when they had not she had supposed Rachel was calling the whole thing off. This cheque was in the nature of a final payment.

Rachel stared at the cheque again. She would have liked to have torn it into shreds there and then, but she wanted it intact to give to the Marquesa.

For the rest of the morning she could settle to nothing. The Marquesa's letter had renewed all her guilty concern about the birth certificate and the bank book upstairs, and she could no longer pretend that they were not there. Something would have to be done. But what?

At last she decided what she would have to do. It meant going back to Portugal, it meant confronting the Marquesa again, but at least that way she could

164

dispose of the other things at one and the same time. And if she saw Luis—well, after these weeks of separation she was calm again and would be able to face him with assurance.

Rachel flew to Portugal at the end of the following week. When she arrived in Lisbon she had to make arrangements about hiring a car to take her to Mendao, and as there was no vehicle available until the following day she spent the night in the airport hotel.

She arrived at the *quinta* at about eleven-thirty the following morning feeling hot and sticky and totally unprepared to face the intimidating presence of the Marquesa.

She had the driver drop her at the gate marked *Privado* and walked up the drive to the house. It was amazing how clearly her memory had served her. She remembered every small detail, and a little ripple of anticipation ran down her spine.

Luisa, the housekeeper, answered her ring and regarded her in astonishment. 'Senhora Trevellyan!' she exclaimed. 'What are you doing here?'

Rachel took a deep breath. 'I've come to see the Senhora Marquesa, Luisa. Is she at home?'

Luisa glanced behind her nervously. *'Sim, senhora.* The Senhora Marquesa is as you say—at home. But she is not well, *senhora.'*

Rachel frowned. 'Why? What's wrong with her?'

Luisa seemed to realise she was keeping a guest waiting on the doorstep and stepping back indicated that Rachel should enter the coolness of the hall. It was a relief to get out of the hot sun, and Rachel entered the cloistered coolness gratefully. Then she turned back to the housekeeper. 'Now—what is it? What is wrong with the Senhora Marquesa?'

'Don't you—don't you know, *senhora?'*

'*Me?*' exclaimed Rachel in surprise. 'How should I know?'

Luisa spread her hands anxiously. 'I do not know, *senhora*,' she murmured unhappily.

Rachel sighed. 'What is it? Luisa, what are you talking about?'

'Who is there, Luisa?'

Rachel would have recognised the Marquesa's cultured tones anywhere. That cold inflection was just as much in evidence, and for a brief moment Rachel wished she had not come.

The housekeeper turned in agitation. '*Esta o* Senhora Trevellyan, Senhora Marquesa!' she replied uncomfortably.

The Marquesa came down the stairs slowly, supporting herself with the handrail. Even to Rachel's sun-blinded eyes she looked pale and weary, and when she saw Rachel a spasm of pain acrossed her face. She halted two or three stairs up and looked across the hall at the English girl, and then she said: 'You may leave us, Luisa!' in stiff, unnatural tones.

Luisa took one last look at both of them and then scuttled away, clearly not happy about leaving her employer with this unexpected visitor. After she had closed a door behind her, the Marquesa spoke again. 'Well, *senhora!*' she said heavily. 'Have you come to gloat?'

Rachel's lips parted. 'Gloat, Senhora Marquesa?'

'Yes, gloat! That is the right word, is it not? I have not been so long in Portugal that I have forgotten the word which means to feast one's eyes on!'

Rachel shook her head. 'I'm afraid I don't understand you, Senhora Marquesa.'

'Don't you?' The Marquesa's lips twisted. 'I'm sure you do. But you're too clever to let me see it.' She looked beyond Rachel to the door. 'Are you alone?'

Rachel wondered whether she had missed something here. Of course she was alone. Why shouldn't she be alone? Who was there to accompany her? She felt confused. What was wrong with the Marquesa? Was this perplexing conversation a symptom?

Speaking carefully, she said: 'Yes, I'm alone, Senhora Marquesa. I—I—Luisa tells me you have not been well.'

The Marquesa came down the last few stairs to stand in the hall. She was wearing a long hostess gown, but her hair was without its usual immaculate elegance, and there was something faintly pitiable about her. Rachel shook her head again. That was the last adjective she would have expected to use to describe this haughty little woman.

'Come,' the Marquesa said now. 'We cannot talk here. We will go into the *sala*.'

The huge *sala* was shadowy. Shutters guarded the windows and the light was filtered on to the exquisite ornamentation. It seemed, Rachel thought rather resignedly, that all the important punctuation marks of her life were to take place within these four walls.

The Marquesa seemed tired. She sought one of the high-backed chairs and sank into it weakly. Rachel stood before her wishing there was something she could do to help her, but she didn't as yet know what was wrong.

'So!' The old lady summoned all her composure. 'Why are you here, *senhora*? Haven't you done enough?'

Rachel ignored the implications of the Marquesa's words. She fumbled in her handbag and drew out the letter which she had received from the Marquesa ten days before. She stepped forward and placed the letter and the cheque in the Marquesa's lap.

The Marquesa picked them up in surprise. She

looked at the cheque and then flicked open the page of her own handwriting. 'Why are you giving me these, *senhora*?' she asked, rather hoarsely.

Rachel was disturbed at the reaction the cheque and letter had had. If anything the Marquesa looked paler than before, and her fingers moved in nervous agitation.

Rachel gave a helpless movement of her shoulders and then drew Joanna Portreath's birth certificate out of her handbag. She went forward again and handed it, and Malcolm's bank book, to the old Marquesa.

There was silence for several minutes. The Marquesa opened the time-worn certificate with trembling hands and read it silently. Then she opened Malcolm's bank book and did the same. After she had examined them she laid them in her lap and just sat there, staring at them.

Rachel grew anxious. What was wrong now? Surely the Marquesa realised that these were the originals.

But then a thought struck her. The certificate was genuine, that was obvious, but like the negative of a film, other copies could be printed. It was all there at the Central Registry just waiting for anyone to check up on it. No documentation was necessary except as proof.

'Senhora Marquesa——' she began, only to be interrupted by the old lady.

'Why have you brought this to me?' she demanded. 'I did not need proof to know such a document existed.'

'You don't understand, Senhora Marquesa——'

'Oh, but I do. This cheque I sent you wasn't enough. You're a young woman, of course, *senhora*. Your needs are greater than those of a man past his prime——'

'*No!*' Rachel was horrified. 'That's not why I came!'

'Then why did you come? If it was not to gloat and it was not to increase your demands——'

'*My* demands?' Rachel caught her breath on a sob. 'I knew nothing about it. I—I only discovered it by accident when I was going through Malcolm's papers!'

'Then I repeat—why are you here? Did—did Luis send you?'

'Luis?' Rachel felt really out of her depth now. 'No, of course Luis didn't send me. He knows nothing about this from me.'

'Ah, I see. You told him you were coming to effect a reconciliation, I suppose.'

'A reconciliation?' Rachel put a dazed hand to her forehead. 'What on earth are you talking about?'

The Marquesa was trembling. 'I realise I am not being very coherent, *senhora*, but spare me the dramatics! Very well. You say Luis didn't send you, that he knows nothing about this. Then why are you here?'

Rachel stepped forward again. 'I came to return the certificate, and the money, too, if you'll have it.'

The Marquesa put a hand to her head now. 'And of course, Luis's appearance had nothing to do with this sudden bout of conscience!'

'Luis's appearance?' Rachel stared at her. 'I haven't seen Luis. How could I? I only arrived in Portugal yesterday afternoon?'

'You arrived in Portugal yesterday afternoon?'

'That's right.'

'And you haven't seen Luis?' The Marquesa rose unsteadily to her feet. 'Oh, how can I believe you?'

'It's the truth! Rachel was indignant. 'I don't tell lies. And nor do I want your money! I'm young, I can work. I don't need that kind of support.'

The Marquesa's eyes were still disturbingly penetrating in spite of her physical weakness. 'If only I could believe you!' she breathed.

Rachel spread her hands desperately. 'You can! But why should it be so important to you?'

The Marquesa moved her head slowly from side to side. 'Because two days ago Luis left for England to find you!'

CHAPTER ELEVEN

Now it was Rachel who felt weak, whose legs felt they would not continue to support her. The Marquesa's face swam dizzily before her eyes and she grasped a nearby chair rather desperately. She had left the hotel very early that morning and the heat in the car coming here had been overpowering. That was what it was, she told herself severely—the heat. She hadn't really heard the Marquesa say that Luis had gone to England to find her, had she?

'I—I——' she began weakly, but she got no further. The Marquesa was by her side, a firm hand propelling her down into the chair, pressing her head down to her knees.

'Relax, *senhora*!' she said calmly. 'Luisa! Luisa! *Venha ca!*'

The housekeeper appeared so swiftly Rachel suspected she had been listening outside the door to assure herself that nothing untoward happened to her mistress.

'The *senhora* is feeling faint,' said the Marquesa when Luisa opened the door. 'Bring us some coffee—oh, and some sandwiches. *Depressa!*'

'*Sim, senhora.*' Luisa cast a startled look in Rachel's direction and then hurried away. When she came back some few minutes later with a tray Rachel was resting her head back against the stiff upholstery and the Marquesa was seated close by.

'Will the *senhora* be staying to lunch, Senhora Marquesa?' Luisa asked, placing the tray on a low table beside her employer.

'Yes, of course, Luisa. I think you had better make

up a room for her also. The *senhora* will not be returning home this evening.'

Rachel felt too enervated to protest, and Luisa bowed and walked to the door. 'Oh, and Luisa!' The Marquesa was not yet finished.

'*Sim, senhora?*'

'You will prepare a room on the first floor, yes?'

'As you say, Senhora Marquesa.'

After Luisa had gone the Marquesa poured the coffee with a remarkably steady hand and handed a cup to Rachel. Rachel took it nervously, half afraid she would drop something again.

'Have a sandwich.' The Marquesa proffered the plate.

Rachel shook her head. 'Thank you, no, I couldn't.'

'Nonsense, of course you could. A young girl like you. You're much too thin.' She continued to hold out the plate and Rachel had, perforce, to take one, but she felt sure it would choke her.

However, it didn't. The sandwiches were so delicately made that they went down quite easily with several sips of the delicious aromatic coffee, and Rachel eventually had three.

The Marquesa sat opposite her, watching her, sipping her coffee slowly and thoughtfully.

When Rachel finally refused anything else, the Marquesa took her empty cup, replaced it on the tray, and folded her hands. 'Now,' she said, 'we can talk.'

'Yes, Senhora Marquesa.' Rachel had never felt less like talking in her life. 'What—what about?'

'First of all I must tell you that I accept your word about Luis. I do not now believe that you have seen him.'

'You mean he—*is* in England?' Rachel stared at the other woman.

'Of course. I do not lie either, *senhora.*'

'No. No, of course not.' Rachel shook her head dazedly. 'But why? Why is he there?'

'We will come to that in a moment. First of all, I want to tell you about your husband.'

'That's not necessary——'

'Oh, but it is. You see——' The Marquesa paused. 'You see, when Malcolm's mother died the certificate fell into his hands. Until then no one had known the truth.'

'That you were his cousin?' ventured Rachel quietly.

'Yes, that's right. My—my mother was his mother's sister, as you've no doubt guessed. She was, so I believe, a kind and generous girl. Just before the First World War, she met and fell in love with a young man whom her father totally rejected. He was a man—if I dare to say it—like Malcolm. He was cold and cruel and insensitive, and Rosemary—that was my mother, of course—couldn't persuade him to change his mind. Then—then——' The Marquesa was obviously finding this part of her story hard to tell. 'Then—she became pregnant. Oh, I don't excuse her. She shouldn't have—have done what she did. But it was too late then for recriminations. She went to her father and told him what had happened. He was incensed. I believe he beat her. They planned, the young man and my mother, to run away together, to elope. But war broke out and he joined the Army before they could make any arrangements. Then, within a month of him going to France, he was killed and Rosemary was completely without hope.'

Rachel felt a tremendous sense of compassion for the lonely girl. She could imagine what Malcolm's grandfather had been like. She could imagine his rage when he discovered his daughter wanted to marry someone who didn't agree with his conceptions of what her husband should be. And later, when he found she was pregnant...

'Well,' went on the Marquesa heavily, 'I was born. Elizabeth, Malcolm's mother, was married by this time but apparently unable to have children. She and her husband agreed to care for me—there was no question of adoption in those days. Then Malcolm was born, and the rest you know.'

'And Rosemary?' asked Rachel quietly.

'She died within a year of my being born. They said it was consumption, but I've never believed that. I think she just died of a broken heart.'

Rachel shook her head. 'How terrible!'

'Yes.' The Marquesa sighed. 'I don't suppose I thought a great deal about the fact of my illegitimacy until Malcolm discovered it. He wrote to me, quite nice letters at first, and I thought he just wanted to be friendly. Ricardo, that was my husband, was ill, and I was glad of someone to confide my anxieties to.' She curled her fingers into a ball. 'But then Malcolm began making demands. Just small ones at first; in the nature of loans to tide him over difficult situations. It wasn't until much later that I began to see what was happening.'

Rachel gripped the arms of her chair. 'But why did you invite him to Mendao?'

'Invite him? I didn't invite him.' The Marquesa spoke vehemently. 'Malcolm was ill, as you know. He said he needed to rest and recuperate. He said if I would just allow him to come and stay for a while, he'd make no further demands on me.'

'But of course that wasn't the end, was it?' murmured Rachel gently.

'Oh, no. No!' The Marquesa dragged a handkerchief from her sleeve and pressed it to her lips. 'No, you're right. Things just got worse.'

'So you stayed at the Alejentos' deliberately?'

'Yes and no. I was ill; I was sick with worry. You see—Luis knew none of this. I have never confided in anyone, not even Ricardo.'

'I see.' Rachel bent her head. 'And the day Malcolm came to Alcorado? That was the final confrontation?'

'Oh, yes.' The Marquesa raised her eyes to the ceiling in mute remembrance. 'What a terrible, *terrible* day that was.'

Rachel nodded. 'If you don't want to talk about it——'

'No. No, I must tell you. Malcolm came to the *sala* where Manuela and I were sewing. I was horrified to see him. I couldn't imagine why he had come.' She tugged distractedly at the handkerchief. 'He—he came right out with it. He told the Alejentos that I was—was a—a bastard!' Her voice almost broke. 'They were flabbergasted, too. They thought he was lying, but I suppose my face gave me away. There was the most terrible row. I thought Carlos, Manuela's husband, would kill him. But Malcolm said that was just the beginning. He said that he would make sure everyone learned of the parentage of the Marquesa de Mendao!'

Rachel felt sick. It was worse than even she had suspected. She had not realised he had revealed everything to the Alejentos. No wonder Senhora Alejento had treated her with such distaste.

The Marquesa's shoulders sagged. 'Then—then, of course, there was Luis.'

'What about Luis?' Belatedly Rachel realised how easily she had spoken Luis's name.

'Malcolm said that Luis was involved with you—that he had tried to make love to you!'

'Oh, no!'

Now Rachel understood why Malcolm had not objected those last two occasions when Luis had sought her presence. They had been his evidence, indisputable facts that could be twisted to mean so many things.

'Oh, yes. And—and Amalia was there to hear it.'

Rachel shook her head. 'But—but surely they didn't believe him!'

'No. No, I don't believe they did—at first.'

'What do you mean—at first?'

The Marquesa shook her head impatiently. 'Nothing, nothing. Well, there it is. The whole sorry mess.' She moved her shoulders helplessly. 'Malcolm had overreached his strength; the attack he had was brief but fatal. Carlos laid him on the couch, but it was too late. He must have died instantly.'

Rachel rose to her feet. It was an incredible story, but it fitted the facts so well. Everything was clear now. She turned back to the Marquesa. 'So Luis learnt the truth, too.'

The Marquesa nodded. 'Yes. He was—very angry. He said I should have confided in him from the beginning—that he would have dealt with Malcolm himself. But I doubt whether anyone could have reasoned with Malcolm. He was totally selfish.'

Rachel heaved a sigh. 'And you say—Luis is in England? Why? Why?'

The Marquesa made a casual gesture. 'He wanted to find out how much you had known about—about everything.'

'I see.' Rachel's spirits plummeted. She might have known it would be something like that. 'He knew about the cheque you sent me?'

'Not at once, no. He—it was when he found out about that that things came to a head between us.'

'Oh!' Rachel could imagine Luis's reactions. She had had the cheque ten days. No doubt he thought she had cashed it. Or was it possible to find out about such things? She supposed it must be. She plucked nervously at the strap of her handbag. 'Well, that's that, isn't it?'

The Marquesa looked up at her. 'What do you mean?'

'Well, I've said everything I came to say, and you've been—very kind, talking to me, explaining everything. I—there's no need for me to stay. I feel perfectly all right now.'

'On the contrary, of course you must stay, tonight at least.' The Marquesa was adamant. 'I wouldn't dream of allowing you to return to England today. Besides, I doubt very much whether you would be able to get a flight. It's very busy at this time of the year.'

Rachel shrugged. 'I'm sure I shall manage.'

'No, you will stay here. I have informed Luisa to that effect. Would you have had her waste her energies unnecessarily?'

Rachel half smiled. 'I suppose not.'

'Very good.' The Marquesa looked relieved. 'And now, if you'll excuse me, I will go and prepare for lunch, Luisa will show you to your room. You might care to wash, too, before sitting down to table.'

During the afternoon Rachel rested in her room. It was a very sumptuous room, even more sumptuous than the rooms she and Malcolm had occupied on the ground floor. Clearly these were the family rooms, and they were cooler and more comfortably furnished.

Rachel's room had blue and gold draperies, and a blue and gold tapestry bedspread. The walls were gold, too, and there were french doors which opened on to the balcony which overlooked a small courtyard below. When she opened these doors and stepped on to the balcony, she realised she was looking down on the courtyard where she had spent so many hours, and her heart raced. Did Luis's apartments open on to this balcony, too? Had he been able to observe her from the shadows up here? It was quite a thought.

Dinner was served in a dining room which would have accommodated thirty people. The Marquesa, dressed completely in black, explained that this was the small dining room, and Rachel felt an uneasy sense of amusement at this piece of information. What an enormous place the *quinta* must be. What would it feel like to be mistress of such an establishment? She was not likely to find out anyway. Besides, it was too big, too impersonal. If ever she got married again, she would want to play some part in the running of her home that meant more than simply issuing orders to an army of servants. But no doubt Amalia found it all very much to her liking. And if one was marrying Luis...

Thinking of Amalia, she ventured quietly: 'It must only be two or three weeks to the wedding, Senhora Marquesa. Will you continue to live at the *quinta* after—afterwards?'

The Marquesa looked at her sharply. 'The wedding? Oh, yes, Luis's wedding.' She drew in her lips. 'No, I don't suppose I shall continue to live at the *quinta* after Luis is married. His wife will be the Marquesa then. I shall merely be the Dowager Marquesa.'

'I see.' Rachel applied herself to the fish soup in the bowl in front of her.

'There is a small house in the grounds, a suitable home for a dowager,' went on the Marquesa. 'Sara and I shall be quite happy there.'

'Oh, yes, Senhora Ribialto!' Rachel remembered she had not seen the elderly companion. 'Where is she?'

'Sara is visiting her mother for a few days. She'll be back next week.' The Marquesa smiled. 'I miss her.'

'I expect you do.' Rachel pushed the soup aside.

Talking about Luis had destroyed her appetite.

The meal dragged on. Talk was infrequent and de-sultory, and Rachel was relieved when after the meal the Marquesa excused herself because of a headache.

'You don't mind, do you, *senhora*?' she queried, al-most gently. 'I will see you in the morning.'

'No, I don't mind.' Rachel stood as the other woman walked across the room. 'But I shall be leaving tomor-row.'

'Of course, of course.' The Marquesa opened the door. '*Boa noite, senhora. Ate amanha!*'

Rachel herself went to bed soon after nine-thirty, but she couldn't sleep. The *quinta* aroused too many mem-ories, not all of them unpleasant ones, and she found herself wondering what it would be like when Amalia was mistress here. The thought of Amalia as Luis's wife made her restless, and unable to stay in bed under such stress, she got up and walked out on to the bal-cony.

Her cotton nightdress blew against her legs in the cool breeze and she felt much better out here. Fortu-nately, she had brought an overnight case with her in case of emergencies, but she had not expected to stay overnight at the *quinta*.

She looked down into the courtyard below. There was no moon tonight and everywhere was in darkness. But then, in that shadowy gloom, something moved.

She drew back, half afraid that she had been seen, but it did not seem likely. All the same, she couldn't help wondering who it could be, and a prickle of ap-prehension alerted her nerve ends. Apart from the ser-vants, she and the Marquesa were alone in the *quinta*, after all, and she was sure it could not be a servant prowling around in the darkness. So who was it?

She moved silently to the balcony rail and took a

second look. Perhaps she had been mistaken, perhaps it had been a trick of the light.

But no, there was the glow of a cigarette end, and her eyes widened in surprise. Whoever it was was not afraid of being observed; and suddenly she thought of Luis!

She drew back aghast into her bedroom, closing the french doors and leaning against them. It couldn't be Luis, could it? Her palms felt moist. She had resigned herself to not seeing him, relaxed really because she had thought that ordeal had been averted, but if that was him down there she would be almost bound to encounter him in the morning.

Her pulses raced. She had the most ridiculous desire to pack her things, put on her clothes and leave right away, without waiting for the morning, but of course she couldn't do that. Apart from the fact that there was no way she could travel these roads around the *quinta* at night, it would only be the cowardly thing to do. And besides, it would be better to face him and be done with it as live all her life wondering whether her feelings for him had simply been the result of an over-charged imagination.

With a sigh she moved away from the french windows, and as she did so there was a knock at her bedroom door.

Her heart pounded noisily in her ears, so noisily that she was sure it was audible. Who was knocking on her door at this time of night? She looked down at the watch. The pointers were vaguely visible to eyes that had adjusted themselves to the gloom. It was almost midnight.

The knock came again, and she moved jerkily across the room to press her ear against the door. 'Who—who's there?' she asked huskily, and there was a muffled exclamation from whoever it was outside.

'Open the door, Rachel!' said Luis forcefully. 'I have to speak with you!'

Rachel felt frozen to the spot. It must have been Luis down there in the courtyard, but she would never have dreamed that he would come to her bedroom. What did he want? How dared he knock at her door at this time of night? What if any of the servants saw him?

'Go—go away, Luis,' she managed. 'We—we can talk in the morning.'

'Now, Rachel!'

'No. Go away, please! I—I'm tired.'

'I saw you on the balcony, Rachel. You can't sleep and nor can I.'

Rachel looked down at the door handle. Beside it was a keyhole, but there was no key to turn the lock against him.

'Are—are you going to go away, Luis, or do I have to call the servants?' she asked tremulously.

There was another angry expletive and then the door handle turned and Luis propelled it inwards, ignoring her puny efforts to prevent him. Once Rachel saw that she was losing the battle, she scurried across the room to drag the tapestry coverlet from the bed and wrap it closely around her thinly clad body.

Luis came in and closed the door, reaching for the switch which illuminated the lamps above the bed. Then he leant against the door, looking across at her with weary impatience. 'Oh, Rachel,' he said, shaking his head. 'Why have you come here?'

Rachel said nothing; she was trembling so much she was amazed the coverlet didn't just fall from her thin shoulders. But she looked at Luis, and what she saw filled her with despair. Her feelings hadn't changed. She was in love with him. But his face mirrored his irritation that she should have dared to come back to his house.

Luis straightened. In a black shirt and pants, he looked thinner than she remembered, and there were lines of weariness beside his mouth. 'Are you afraid of me, Rachel?' he asked.

Rachel tried to calm herself. Being nervous wasn't going to do any good. 'No,' she said, with assumed composure. 'No, I'm not afraid of you, Luis.'

'Then by God, you should be!' he said between his teeth.

Rachel paled. 'Why?' She glanced round. 'I don't believe you'd touch me here. I could scream, and there are servants——'

He swore in his own language. 'That is not my intention—to touch you! On the contrary, I find you totally—totally——' He shook his head mutely and turned away, raking his scalp with his nails. Rachel watched him helplessly, unable to understand his mental torment, unable to bear this obvious agony of mind.

She stepped forward, reaching out a hand to touch his shoulder. Even through the fine material of his shirt, his skin felt fiery to her touch. 'Luis——' she began tentatively, but even she was not prepared for what happened next.

Luis turned, his face tortured, and with a groan he pulled her into his arms. She had been close to him before, but never as close as this, conscious of the throbbing heat of his body even through the thickness of the cover she had thrown around herself. But his hands pushed the offending coverlet aside, seeking the smooth, fragile bones of her shoulders and throat, sliding round her neck to grip almost chokingly.

'Oh, Rachel!' he muttered savagely. 'I could kill you——'

Rachel raised her hands to grip his wrists and as she

did so the coverlet fell unheeded in a heap at their feet. 'Why, Luis?' she whispered huskily, bending her head to touch his wrists with her lips, uncaring for the moment that this situation ought not to be allowed to develop. 'What have I done?'

Luis's fingers loosened their grip. An expression of such longing crossed his face that her knees felt weak. And then his mouth was on hers and all coherent thought ceased. His hands slid round her back, moulding her body to his, making her overwhelmingly conscious of his need of her, destroying her good intentions to remain calm. Her arms slid round his waist, and she pressed herself against him.

Luis was muttering to her in his own language between kisses, burying his face in the hollow of her neck, in her hair, caressing her hips, holding her against him.

But then warning bells began to ring in Rachel's head. There was no doubt in her mind now that Luis wanted her, and she wanted him, she *loved* him, but not even for love could she become his mistress.

With a little sob, she tore herself away from him, and with a heavy sigh Luis sank down on to the bed and buried his head in his hands. '*Por amor de Deus,*' he groaned, 'what am I going to do?'

Rachel stared at him. 'I think you'd better go,' she said chokingly.

He looked up at her, his face haggard. 'Yes. Yes, of course, that is what I must do.' But he made no move.

Rachel hugged herself, trying to make the cotton nightdress a less revealing garment. 'I—it was as much my fault as yours.'

Luis's eyes narrowed. 'Do you think that makes it any better?' he demanded harshly.

Rachel shrugged. 'I don't know. I've never done this sort of thing before.'

Luis's lips twisted. 'No, I can believe that.'

Rachel didn't like the look on his face. 'I'm tired,' she said. 'Please—go!'

'Why did you do it, Rachel?' Luis might not have heard her.

Rachel frowned. 'Do it? Do what?'

'Come here. Wasn't a letter good enough?'

'No. I wouldn't trust such things to a letter.'

'I see. I wonder why. Malcolm never had such qualms. Or maybe you think you'd like to stay on here—as he did!'

'What are you talking about?' Rachel didn't understand him.

'Doesn't that figure in your plans?'

'Luis, what are you talking about?'

Luis shook his head grimly. 'It's no use, Rachel. You're too late. I know the truth, the Alejentos know the truth. Who else are you threatening to tell?'

Now Rachel understood and she trembled with indignation. 'How—how dare you speak to me like this? I—I've never been so insulted in all my life!'

Luis looked up at her with distaste. 'Why? Are the facts unpalatable?'

'They're not facts.' Rachel drew herself up to her full height. 'If you had taken the trouble to ask your mother before coming here and speaking to me, you'd have learned that this morning I gave her back her birth certificate and the bank book of Malcolm's which contains all the deposits made since—since the certificate fell into his hands.'

Luis sat there transfixed, just staring at her. 'What?'

'It's the truth. Oh, Luis, what do you think I am?'

Luis put a dazed hand to his head. 'You mean—you mean you weren't a party to—to Malcolm's plans?'

'Of course I wasn't. What do you take me for?' Rachel's voice broke on a sob. 'Oh, go away, go away and leave me alone. Go back to Amalia! You needn't worry, I shan't tell her about—about your lapse of conduct!'

She turned away, trying not to burst into tears right there in front of him. She felt so humiliated. And the cotton nightdress was not the sort of garment one could behave in a dignified fashion in without looking completely ridiculous, she felt sure.

'Rachel, Rachel, how can you ever forgive me?' Luis sounded weak with relief. He leant forward and caught her wrist, refusing to release her when she endeavoured to free herself. He drew her compellingly back on to the bed beside him, taking her tear-wet face between his hands. 'Rachel,' he groaned, bending to touch the corner of her mouth with his lips. 'Oh, Rachel, I'm sorry.'

Rachel drew a choking breath. 'You don't have to feel sorry for me,' she declared unsteadily. 'Just go away and leave me alone.'

'No.' He shook his head. 'Not before I try and explain my position.'

'I don't want to hear your position—oh!'

He had closed her lips with his finger and was appealing to her silently. 'Now,' he said, still holding her face firmly, 'you must know now what Malcolm was doing.'

She nodded. 'Your mother told me everything this morning.'

'So?' He raised his eyebrows. 'So you will appreciate my concern for her.'

'I don't see what——'

'Wait!' His eyes narrowed, holding hers. 'I discovered she had written to you some days ago, enclosing a cheque. Is that correct?' Rachel nodded, and he went on: 'I was furious with her for doing so, but she is—how do you say it?—not convinced that you mean to let everything drop now. She was in—suspense? Is that right?'

Rachel sighed. 'She told me.'

'So? Things are worse for her after you leave. After Malcolm's funeral.' He dropped his hands into his lap and bent his head.

Rachel noticed how, when he was emotionally disturbed as now, his accent was more pronounced. But what did he mean?

'How—how were things worse?' she asked, in surprise.

Luis sighed now. 'I will come to that. You must know how I feel about you, Rachel.'

Rachel quivered. She ventured a glance at him and found his eyes upon her. 'No——' she whispered. 'No, I don't know.'

'I am in love with you. I want you, Rachel. For my wife!'

Rachel could not believe it. She put her palms to her burning cheeks and stared blindly down at her knees.

'It's the truth,' he said quietly, still not touching her even though all her senses cried out for him to do so. 'But it was not that simple.' He ran a hand round the back of his neck. 'My mother was totally opposed to any relationship between us. Apart from anything else, I was betrothed to Amalia.'

'Was?' echoed Rachel weakly.

Luis nodded. 'But of course. You do not think I could contemplate marrying Amalia when I feel as I do about you?'

'I don't know what to think.' Rachel timidly put her hand on his knee. He flinched, but still he did not touch her.

'You want I should show you,' he said, rather thickly. 'But I must not touch you until I tell you how

186

these things happen.' He drew an unsteady breath. 'Very well, so much against my mother's wishes I break with Amalia. But that is not the end. In spite of the fact that I love you, there is still the matter of—of——'

'—the blackmail,' prompted Rachel, stroking his thigh.

'Yes.' Luis spoke gruffly. 'I thought I could not marry a woman who had been party to such a thing, particularly when I realised the effect it had had and could still have on my mother. But my feelings for you were stronger than even I imagined. I could think of nothing else. I wanted you, Rachel. So much!'

Rachel shivered. 'Go on.'

'My mother realised this, I think, and that was why she wrote to you. She thought if you accepted the cheque then I could see that you were just as corrupt as—as Malcolm. But even then I could not believe it, not entirely. I didn't want to believe it, you see. So I flew to England to find the truth for myself. Then, of course, you were not there.'

'No,' Rachel nodded.

'I made enquiries, but your neighbours could tell me nothing. All they could give me was the address of your solicitors. I went to them. I explained who I was. And when they could tell me nothing of your whereabouts also, I asked about you—about your marriage to Malcolm—about the reasons behind that marriage. They were reluctant to discuss your affairs, naturally. It is their job to remain unmoved by emotive pleas.' His lips twisted. 'But their clerk was a little more responsive to—persuasion.' He shrugged expressively. 'And when I mentioned the matter of your condition at the time of your marriage——'

'My condition? What condition?' Rachel stared at him in surprise.

Luis shook his head. 'Of course you do not know.

How could you?' He sighed. 'When Malcolm tried to justify his reasons for marrying you to me, he told me that you had had an affair with a young man who had deserted you when you became pregnant, and that after he had helped you by taking responsibility, you had had a miscarriage——'

'Oh, no!' gasped Rachel, in horror. She shook her head dazedly. 'So that explains why you appeared to despise me, why you asked me those rather curious questions at the *quinta*. But it's not true,' she added, a note of anxiety invading her voice.

'I know that now.' Luis was reassuringly gentle. 'I think I guessed it could not be true all along. And when this man—this clerk—told me of your father's financial difficulties ...' He clenched his fists impotently. Then, as though gathering himself again, he went on: 'This afternoon, my mother telephoned the hotel where she knew I was staying. She left a message for me to return here right away as you were here. Can you imagine how I felt? I had just begun to have faith in you, but my mother's message gave me second thoughts. I began to wonder whether in part she had not been right all along, and that you had come here to start the blackmail all over again. I was incensed and desperate. My need for you was such that just now I found myself wondering whether I could bear to marry you anyway.'

'Oh, Luis! I love you.'

And then he touched her. He pressed her back against the soft silk sheets of the bed and covered her mouth with his own, and for several long minutes there was silence in the bedroom.

But at last he dragged himself up and away from her, smoothing his hair and buttoning his shirt with a slight smile on his lips.

'So?' he said. 'When I present you to my mother

tomorrow morning as my *noiva*, my fiancée, I want to do so with a clear conscience.'

Rachel smiled and then sobered. 'But—but what about your mother?' she murmured uneasily. 'Will—will she accept me?'

Luis pulled her up into his arms. 'I admit it will not always be easy,' he murmured into her hair. 'For so long she has been mistress here and Amalia and she would have managed admirably. Amalia has been brought up that way. But you——' He touched her cheek gently. 'You are different, and that is why I fell in love with you. You were so irritating to me, right from the very beginning, and right from the beginning I knew you meant trouble so far as my peace of mind was concerned.'

'Did you mind?'

'At first? Oh, yes. But I couldn't keep away from you, as you may have noticed.' His eyes darkened. 'And nor could I bear to think of you with—with Malcolm.'

'Poor Malcolm.' Rachel could feel sorry for him now. After all, it was because of him that she had found something beyond price.

'Yes, poor Malcolm,' echoed Luis quietly. Then: 'But now I must go. We have an appointment for tomorrow.'

Rachel hesitated. 'And—and you think your mother will—will not be too disappointed?'

'Let us put it this way: she has known so long that you are the only woman I would ever consider marrying that she will no doubt become resigned to the fact that this will be the only way I can beget heirs and she can become a grandmother.'

Rachel felt the hot colour flooding her cheeks. 'I see.'

'And besides, she telephoned me in England this

afternoon and told me you were here. She needn't have done that.'

'No, I suppose not.' Rachel drew back from him reluctantly. 'Don't you think I'll be a big disappointment as—as a Marquesa?'

Luis touched his fingers to her lips. 'Not to me, *amada*,' he whispered. 'Never to me . . .'

And that was all that mattered after all.

JOY
ROMANCE
LOVE

Harlequin Omnibus

THREE love stories in ONE beautiful volume

The joys of being in love...
the wonder of romance...
the happiness that true love brings...

Now yours in the HARLEQUIN OMNIBUS
edition every month wherever
paperbacks are sold.